MW00772022

Ayurveda

*Secrets of Hindu Healing through the
Ayurvedic Diet, Meditation and
Aromatherapy along with a Guide to
Understanding the Yoga Sutras of Patanjali*

© Copyright 2020

All Rights Reserved. No part of this book may be reproduced in any form without permission in writing from the author. Reviewers may quote brief passages in reviews.

Disclaimer: No part of this publication may be reproduced or transmitted in any form or by any means, mechanical or electronic, including photocopying or recording, or by any information storage and retrieval system, or transmitted by email without permission in writing from the publisher.

While all attempts have been made to verify the information provided in this publication, neither the author nor the publisher assumes any responsibility for errors, omissions or contrary interpretations of the subject matter herein.

This book is for entertainment purposes only. The views expressed are those of the author alone, and should not be taken as expert instruction or commands. The reader is responsible for his or her own actions.

Adherence to all applicable laws and regulations, including international, federal, state and local laws governing professional licensing, business practices, advertising and all other aspects of doing business in the US, Canada, UK or any other jurisdiction is the sole responsibility of the purchaser or reader.

Neither the author nor the publisher assumes any responsibility or liability whatsoever on behalf of the purchaser or reader of these materials. Any perceived slight of any individual or organization is purely unintentional.

Contents

PART 1: AYURVEDA... 1

UNLOCKING THE SECRETS OF HINDU HEALING THROUGH THE AYURVEDA DIET, YOGA, AROMATHERAPY, AND MEDITATION..... 1

INTRODUCTION.. 2

CHAPTER 1: WHAT IS AYURVEDA?..................................... 4

CHAPTER 2: AYURVEDA MEDICINE – WHAT IT IS, HOW SAFE, AND HOW EFFECTIVE.. 15

CHAPTER 3: AYURVEDIC LIFESTYLE.................................... 26

CHAPTER 4: AYURVEDIC DIET – WHAT TO EAT AND THE EFFECTS OF AN AYURVEDIC DIET.. 37

CHAPTER 5: AYURVEDIC HERBS, HERBAL MEDICINE AND HEALTH BENEFITS.. 47

CHAPTER 6: AYURVEDA AND YOGA...................................... 58

CHAPTER 7: AROMATHERAPY AND AYURVEDA................... 67

CHAPTER 8: AYURVEDIC MEDITATION................................. 75

CHAPTER 9: AYURVEDA NATURAL BEAUTY TIPS 84

CHAPTER 10: AYURVEDIC RECIPES AND BEVERAGES 91

SUMMARY.. 124

CONCLUSION 126

PART 2: YOGA SUTRAS.. 128

AN ESSENTIAL GUIDE TO UNDERSTANDING THE YOGA SUTRAS OF PATANJALI... 128

INTRODUCTION.. 129

CHAPTER ONE: INTRODUCTION TO YOGA PHILOSOPHY............ 132

HUMBLE ORIGINS 132

THE PHILOSOPHY OF YOGA 133

FORMS OF YOGA 135

THE SPREAD OF YOGA... 136

THE PHASES OF YOGA IN HISTORY 137

SRI PATANJALI'S PHILOSOPHY AND HIS CONTRIBUTION TO YOGA 139

THE CATEGORIES OF PATANJALI'S SUTRAS 140

THE RELEVANCE OF YOGA IN THE PRESENT CENTURY........................ 140

PHYSICAL BENEFITS OF YOGA 141

THE MENTAL BENEFITS OF YOGA... 142

THE EMOTIONAL AND SOCIAL BENEFITS OF YOGA 143

CHAPTER TWO: BACKGROUND OF YOGA SUTRAS —
IMPORTANT CONCEPTS 144

THE CONCEPT OF VRITTI... 144

VRITTI AND CHAKRAS 146

TYPES OF VRITTI.. 147

THE METAPHYSICAL SCHOOLS OF THOUGHT 148

THE DEVELOPMENT OF ADVAITA PHILOSOPHY 151

ADVAITA VEDĀNTA: THE PLANES OF EXISTENCE............................... 152

CHAPTER THREE: SADHANA AND SAMADHI EXPLAINED............ 154

ABHYĀSA AND VAIRĀGYA: SPIRITUAL PRACTICES FOR SADHANA 154

LEVELS OF SADHANA.. 156

THE PLACE OF CONSCIOUSNESS IN SAMĀDHI 157

THE FUNCTIONS OF THE CITTA 158

KINDS OF SAMADHI 159

THE HAZARDS OF SAMĀDHI... 161

CHAPTER FOUR: SAVITARKA VERSUS NIRVITARKA
SAMADHI.. 162

UNDERSTANDING THE SERENITY CALLED SAMĀDHI........................ 162

THE WAY TO ATTAIN SAMADHI 164

LEVELS OF SAMADHI.. 166

THE TEN TYPES OF SAMĀDHI 167

THE DIFFERENCE BETWEEN SABIJA AND NIRBIJA SAMĀDHI 169

CHAPTER FIVE: THE PHILOSOPHY OF SĀDHANĀ AND ITS CONNECTION TO KLEŚA 172

KLEŚA: THE ROOT OF HUMAN SUFFERING 173

COMBATING KLEŚA 178

THE GUṆA AND THEIR PLACE IN YOGIC BELIEF 178

THE INFLUENCE OF THE GUṆA AND FINDING BALANCE 178

KARMĀŚAYA AND THE FRUITS OF KARMA 179

KARMA, REINCARNATION, AND MOKṢA 180

CHAPTER SIX: THE EIGHT FOLD PATH OF YOGA 182

CHAPTER SEVEN: ASANAS, PRANAYAMA, AND PRATYAHARA 191

ASANA AND GYMNASTICS: SIMILAR OR DIFFERENT? 192

BENEFITS OF ASANAS 193

THE THREE MAIN MODIFICATIONS IN PRĀṆĀYĀMA 194

THE FOURTH PRĀṆĀYĀMA 195

BENEFITS OF PRANAYAMA 197

SOME EXAMPLES OF PRANAYAMA 198

FORMS OF PRATYAHARA 200

CHAPTER EIGHT: VIBHOOTI PADA – DHARANA, DHYANA, SAMADHI, AND SAMNYAMA 202

THE DIFFERENCE BETWEEN DHYANA AND AWARENESS 205

THE LINK BETWEEN DHYANA AND SAMADHI 206

CHAPTER NINE: APPLICATION OF THE YOGA SUTRAS IN TODAY'S WORLD 211

TIPS TO CULTIVATING AHIMSA AND FINDING HAPPINESS 212

TIPS TO CULTIVATING SATYA AND LIVING OUR TRUTH 214

TIPS TO PRACTICING ASTHEYA AND SELFLESS SERVICE IN OUR DAILY LIVES 216

TIPS FOR CULTIVATING BRAHMACHARYA AND PRACTICING MODERATION 217

TIPS FOR CULTIVATING GRATITUDE IN OUR DAILY LIVES 219

TIPS FOR CULTIVATING SIMPLICITY IN OUR DAILY LIVES 221

TIPS FOR PRACTICING CONTENTMENT IN OUR DAILY LIVES 222

TIPS TO PRACTICE SELF DISCIPLINE AND PERSEVERANCE IN OUR DAILY LIVES 223

TIPS TO HELP US UNITE WITH OUR TRUE SELVES IN DAILY LIVING 224

TIPS FOR PRACTICING DEVOTION TO GOD IN OUR DAILY LIVES............. 225

HELPFUL TIPS FOR DAILY PRACTICE 226

DO'S AND DON'TS FOR THE PRACTICING YOGI 228

CHAPTER TEN: THE PATH OF TRANSFORMATION – KARMA, VASANA, SIDDHI, AND ANANDA.. 230

THE PRINCIPLES FORMING THE FOUNDATION OF KARMA 231

KARMA IN JAIN PHILOSOPHY 232

RESOLVING KARMA 233

KARMA AND ITS RELATIONSHIP WITH VASANAS 234

FORMS OF VĀSANĀS 236

CONTROLLING AND ERADICATING VĀSANĀS 236

THE EIGHT CLASSICAL SIDDHIS 238

WAYS TO ATTAIN SIDDHI 242

CHAPTER ELEVEN: THE MYSTERY OF PERCEPTION 245

COGNITION VERSUS PERCEPTION: THE ELEPHANTS IN THE ROOM 246

THOUGHT PROCESSES DISSECTED IN THE YOGA SUTRAS 247

CHAPTER TWELVE: THE HIGHEST STATE OF BLISS – KAIVALYA... 255

MASTERING KAIVALYA: THE PATH OF THE KEVALIN 256

SEVEN STAGES OF THE DISCOVERY OF REALITY 258

CONCLUSION 261

HERE'S ANOTHER BOOK BY KIMBERLY MOON THAT YOU MIGHT LIKE.. 265

REFERENCES 266

Part 1: Ayurveda

Unlocking the Secrets of Hindu Healing Through the Ayurveda Diet, Yoga, Aromatherapy, and Meditation

Introduction

The purpose of this book is to introduce the secrets of Hindu healing through the practice of Ayurveda. Ayurveda was first established over 5,000 years ago and recognized as an ancient medical system—the oldest in the world. The practice of medicine and the establishment of various other medical systems that have derived from Ayurveda has transformed, but the constancy and practice of Ayurveda have stood the test of time.

In today's world, people are more aware of their environment and how it affects their health and mental attitude. The ups and downs of life and relationships can sometimes stress the mind, body, and spirit, which can be unsettling.

In the practice of Ayurveda, everything is a part of the same awareness, and it acknowledges that humans are much more than their physical body; they are multidimensional beings that have emotions and intuition. This science acknowledges the importance of the environment for health.

The following chapters will discuss all the elements that are Ayurveda: what is Ayurveda and its history; Ayurvedic medicine; identifying our individual *dosha*; and how yoga, meditation, the use of herbs, and aromatherapy bring our mind, body, and spirit together in balance.

Chapter 1: What is Ayurveda?

Development and Origin of Ayurveda

The history of medicine is intriguing. It is the account of the struggle against a disease that has been waged for centuries. Civilization has advanced, and the pattern of diseases has changed. Due to these changes, medical science has evolved as well.

Ayurveda (pronounced aye-your-VAY-duh) is the oldest health system in the world, an ancient medical system from India established 5,000 years ago. It is the system of health from which Western and Chinese Herbology originated from. Its complete understanding of the human body was much ahead of its time, and it ultimately spanned along what is known as the Silk Road. It made its way east from India to China and then to Indonesia. Ayurvedic texts were translated by 700 CE to Chinese and Chinese scholars who came to India to study in 700 CE. Ayurveda had a tremendous influence on Chinese medicine.

The science of Ayurveda also spread west across the Persian Empire, up to Europe and further east to Egypt and then south to Somalia. Traders spoke of the knowledge of the herbs from India inspired by Ayurveda. (Ketabi, 2017)

The information was further acknowledged by the empires of the Romans and Greeks, which is the foundation for European medicine, as well as Herbology.

Ayurveda is a Sanskrit word that means "knowledge of life". In order to realize complete health, you have to know all the aspects of your life. This system of healing goes beyond the physical and merges the medical, mental, emotional, spiritual, and metaphysical, which are all interrelated. It merges the science of psychology, philosophy, and spirituality. (Ketabi, 2017)

Ayurveda has endured as a distinctive entity from distant antiquity to the present. It is said to be a perpetual science that, firstly, was in the universal consciousness. It was then given from the creator through meditation to the primeval Indian mystics. The fundamentals of the Ayurvedic system have remained true and have not changed. These fundamentals are founded on inherent causes. It originates from Sanskrit as two separate words—Ayur meaning "life" and Veda, meaning "knowledge". To achieve the balance of Ayurveda, you need to have total knowledge of your life.

The beginnings of Ayurveda go deep into ancient times. In the Bronze Age, 3300-1300 BCE, the Indus Valley, today's Pakistan, civilization thrived. During this time, many of the spices and foods that are related to Ayurvedic cooking, such as mung beans, rice, ginger, turmeric, and urad dal (also known as black lentils) were grown during this period.

Later, a shift of the center of civilization moved to the Ganges basin. There, the people identified as Arya or noble ones. They practiced a life-affirming devoutness summarized in the Vedas. Written in a primeval form of Sanskrit between 500 and 1000 BCE (Before Common Era), the Vedas are thought to be the oldest written data in human history and acclaims the essentials of life, expressly of Mother Earth and the plants and animals that inhabit her as well as fire, wind, and water. Today there are many herbs used in Ayurveda—as well as those herbs that are not known to us now but were originally explained in the Vedas. (Nation Ayurvedic Medical Association, 2019)

In 800 BCE, Punarvasu Atrya founded the first Ayurvedic medical school. This was an influence on Charaka, a scholar who lived in 700 BCE. He was one of the principal contributors to Ayurveda and is the author of *Charaka Samhita*, a book that defines 1,500 plants and recognizes 350 of the plants as valuable to medicine. The *Charaka Samhita* is thought to be the first major text of Ayurveda. The Susruta Samhita was written approximately 100 years later and is the basis of modern surgery. It is still referred to today.

As the Vedic or Gangetic society entered 600 BCE, the Iron Age, an atmosphere of reason and awakening emerged over the known world. Aristotle and Plato gave their teachings in Greece, the Middle East was taught by Hebrew prophets, and in Northern India, the Buddha.

Born around 500 BCE, the Buddha was a devotee of Ayurveda. It was Ayurveda that accompanied the spread of Buddhism over Asia. During a time when there was virtually very little known about the human body and mind, the cause of diseases, indications of imbalance, ways to achieve emotional, spiritual and mental wellbeing was explained by Ayurveda.

The Indian manner of healing did away with ancient superstitions and gained deep reasoning, clarity, and meaningful philosophical basis that have described Ayurveda since. From this awareness of reason, the writings of Ayurveda, particularly *Sushrut Samhita* and *Charak Samhita* rose. Over many centuries of fine-tuning and clarification, these writings began to have their present form during the Golden Age of India (320 to 550 CE (Common Era)) under the Gupta Empire.

India has always been an enticing prospect to invaders and traders because of the gems, spices, peacocks, and rich textiles. India has been able to learn from the influences of the outside world while maintaining its own culture due to its intrinsic tolerance and acceptance.

Ayurveda remained the medicine of choice for the major portion of people, even with the invasions by the Mongols and Genghis Khan in the thirteenth century and the Mughals in the sixteenth century. During the reign of Emperor Akbar, Ayurveda was enjoyed equally as the Unani or Arabic medicine. (Nation Ayurvedic Medical Association, 2019)

When the British came in to rule India, the medical system was considered archaic and no longer allowed. It disappeared from public use but continued to be practiced in private homes, even when the British forced Western medicine upon the Indian people. As an "underground" medicine, Ayurveda was thought to become a "kitchen medicine." Eventually, the wisdom of Ayurvedic medicine resurfaced and extended past the boundaries of India and was embraced worldwide as people were drawn to Ayurveda's methods that have exceeded the test of time.

Ayurveda places importance on the effects of how each season and diet balances the body. At various times of the day, distinctive attributes or doshas prevail, as well as psychological changes that occur in the body during the seasons. Ayurveda knows that the mainstay of good health is to move with the times and climate because we are a microcosm of what occurs in the environment.

Foods that are packaged, refrigerated, and reheated contain very little important nutrients. When the fuel you ingest is poor, the immune system cannot function at optimal capacity. *Vyadhishamatva* knows that immunity or forgiveness of disease is a point for the beginning of good health. Improving the immune system is achieved by eating the best food.

In Ayurveda, everything is a part of the same awareness and acknowledges that humans are much more than their physical body. They are beings that are multidimensional and have emotions and intuition. This science acknowledges the importance of the environment for health. It is difficult to maintain good health when our world is assaulted by constant development, the disappearance of forests that are cut down en masse, and the practices applied to farming that disrespect sentient beings. (Hope-Murray, 2013)

Ayurved delves into the multifaceted mind-body link and transports you back to balance. It is such as the beatific feeling you experience after you are lying in the corpse pose, *shabasana.* It is possible to enjoy that feeling all the time, and this book will teach you how. Not only will Ayurveda be explained, but how to apply it to transform your health and happiness for your life. (Ketabi, 2017)

Based on the belief that health can be attained by creating a balance of mind, body, and spirit, Ayurveda is the science that is a sister of yoga. Our health can be changed through our awareness of our environments. The foundation of health is attaining the balance of mind and body. It is not as simple as one is to believe it is.

There are particular practices, guidelines, remedies, and recipes to help attain that balance. Guidelines do differ for each person, and through the year they change, over both seasons and your entire life. It may sound a bit complex, but the knowledge you receive will change your life, and it is worth it to achieve wellbeing that will last over your life.

Ayurveda is a science that is truly holistic and supported from the birth of life's end. The Ayurvedic way of life is to maximize lifespan through intervention by optimizing health and care for the environment as well as the body, mind, and spirit. The importance is preventing illness and the promotion of health, in an all-inclusive way of treatment. (Hope-Murray, 2013)

This is not a traditional method of healing. A multitude of lifestyle choices is opened when a total analysis of body type, types of imbalances, psychological propensities, and dietary requirements are established. The benefits of Ayurveda have reached far past the initial principles that were the concept of the ancient rishis. The basis of this system is for wellbeing that lasts a lifetime, and that

Nature and the human mind, body, and spirit are attuned. This attunement is through the choices that are consciously made each day, and the body-mind response is strengthened.

Our lives have reached an incredible level of stress from speed, electronic gadgets, and complications that taking the time to be in tune with Nature has either been overlooked or forgotten. This will change in relearning the basics of wellness. Anyone who wants to look honestly and deeply enough, this encompasses an awakening that starts with questions people have asked for centuries, such as *Who am I? How do I interrelate to Nature and its massive realm? What is this body that I occupy?* Ayurveda gives an entirely practical, thoroughly thought-out way to answer these questions. (Ketabi, 2017)

The Western thesis has been the long tradition for linking human nature and Nature, but there has been nothing as deep and systematic as Ayurveda. Although it may be the world's oldest system for health, Ayurveda is by no means dead. In a time where everything in life speeds up much too quickly, Ayurveda teaches us the advantages of going slowly and discovering our natural biorhythms and giving them respect. All of us want to be healthy and maintain it, but as the expectancy of life lengthens, the average person as they age spends anywhere from eight to ten years fighting disability and disease. One of the ways that illness can be overcome and maintained is through long-term strategies for wellness. There is a vast audience of those who are new to Ayurveda and are in serious need of having such a strategy. (Ketabi, 2017)

Swastha, in Sanskrit, is the word that describes health and is "to be established in self." Awareness of health in each part of our day can be achieved through meditation.

There are specialties in Ayurveda, as in Western medicine. The eight Ayurvedic medicine are Internal medicine (kaya chikitsa), General surgery (shalya tantra), Toxicology (agada tantra), Fertility treatment (vajikarana), Childhood diseases or pediatrics (bala tantra), Psychiatry (bhuta vidya), Head and neck disease (salakya tantra), and Geriatrics rejuvenation (rasayana).

Western Medicine and Ayurvedic Medicine

Ayurvedic medicine is meant to complement Western medicine, not replace it. Its approach is to prevent the disease from appearing, whereas Western medicine concentrates on the symptom of an illness or disease and deals with it after the disease has already materialized. Acute conditions and trauma are treated by highly advanced Western medicine and its technical sophistication. However, the connections of the symptoms that Western medicine treats don't have knowledge of the reasons why symptoms or the disease keep happening over and over again.

Ayurvedic medicine defends that our physical condition is reflective of our mental state and vice versa. People who are overweight will be asked about what they may be holding on to by an Ayurvedic practitioner. If someone is unable to sleep, it may be recommended that they walk in nature. Liver problems? What is the unsolved anger issue that they're having?

Suggestions about what to do for your conditions will not be offered until your childhood, daily schedule, eating habits, and even dreams are told to an Ayurvedic practitioner. All of the elements that may have caused the problem are studied and looked at, not just the problem itself. This is a holistic approach, all-inclusive of the entire person—mind, body, and spirit.

Surgeries, medical examinations, and other medical procedures are included in Ayurvedic medicine, but these are less practiced than dietary and lifestyle advice that is what Ayurvedic medicine is today.

Many Ayurvedic herbs are pure and very effective, while others have a lesser effect. Just as in using any other type of medicine, it is crucial to be aware of what is being ingested into the body rather than taking medication or herbs just because it says it's Ayurvedic.

However, the most effective medicine that can be ingested is the food on your plate.

Yoga

Yoga is practiced by 30 percent of Americans, and that figure is rising. With the growth of yoga, more people have become interested in its sister practice, Ayurveda. These two sciences were intended to be practiced in unison by the Vedas. However, Ayurveda has only begun to get some attention and the spotlight that has been on yoga.

In taking a yoga class, if it was to become one with a divine source, you are practicing yoga. If taking a yoga class was to become healthier and balanced, then that is the practice of Ayurveda.

Yoga is to attain enlightenment on a spiritual level, while Ayurveda is practiced to realize health. Many people who take yoga classes are probably practicing Ayurveda because they are looking for the health benefits rather than being one with the divine.

Ayurveda in Present Day

Today, Ayurveda has risen in popularity, surely with those who have an interest in integrative and Traditional medicine. There is an imperative need that has put Ayurveda at the forefront of today's healthcare that has now become disturbingly expensive. People are frustrated by their medical care depending almost solely on surgery and drugs, many of which have drastic and sometimes fatal side effects where other parts of the body are affected and are weakened. Because of this, people have searched for healthier and safer alternatives. (Ketabi, 2017)

Ayurveda is practiced around the world, not just in India. Self-oil massaging, dry brushing and oil pulling have now gone more mainstream. More of the knowledge of the food combination and digestion comes from the knowledge of Ayurvedic medicine; the anti-inflammatory, anti-aging, and antidepressant Tumeric (a spice in the Ayurvedic diet) is now being sold in capsules.

Ayurvedic Panchakarma, the annual treatment to detoxify and rejuvenate health, has thousands of people traveling to India every year to participate in this treatment. Millions of people practice Ayurveda and don't even know they are doing so.

The cookie-cutter method to health has given Americans the less than best possible state of health. Ayurveda's whole-body method to health sees the whole person, not just a single symptom. This approach has drawn people to Ayurveda for its benefits. As is usually the case, most doctors do not take the time to get to know their patients, aside from an examination and the dispensing of medications. After that, people are left to their own devices to learn what the root cause of their disease is. Ayurveda can assist in solving those mysteries.

In the practice of Ayurveda, prescriptions and pills are not what health is about; it is a lifestyle that is a regiment of balance and harder to follow than filling a prescription and taking the medication. To maintain Ayurveda, it needs personal responsibility and can be much more effective.

One of the beliefs of Ayurveda is that the uniqueness of the individual is the secret of their wellbeing. The distinctive genetic makeup we all have, lifestyles, metabolisms, mental qualities, physiologies, and many other factors decide our medical and dietary needs. The idea of being an individual with unique problems has become the point of why we have grown tired of health statements that are general in content, and thus, left us feeling defeated and exhausted.

There is no single guideline that can work for all because we are all different beings with unique makeup and needs according to Ayurveda. This conclusion may seem like an apparent finding, but it really took thousands of years, an epidemic of obesity, and a health emergency for many of us to discover it. Ayurveda was really ahead of its time.

As you read through this book, you will begin to understand the connection between mind and body. The book will cover all the different factors that are Ayurveda:

Ayurvedic Medicine – You will read about what it is, its effectiveness, how safe it is, and how it is the oldest system of medicine in the world. It is plant-based and is a combination of herbs as well as essential oils. The chapters about both of these elements will explain how each one, individually and combined, will bring you the health and wellbeing you seek.

Ayurvedic Lifestyle – You will fill out a body type questionnaire to see which dosha or body type you fall into—Vata, Pitta or Kapha. Your abilities, attributes, state of mind, conditions, or afflictions that pertain to you will be part of the questionnaire.

The myths and misconceptions are outlined for you to understand and become more knowledgeable about Ayurvedic medicine and the practice of Ayurveda.

You'll also learn and understand mental and physical characteristics, as well as the traits associated with each dosha and which is your most dominant type.

Ayurvedic Diet – Each body type has its own list of foods, as well as vitamins and minerals that complement their dosha. The chapter will list foods for each body type, as well as the diet that will be most effective for each. Throughout the book, there will be recommendations as to what is Ayurvedic for weight loss.

Ayurvedic Plants and Herbs – The chapter will focus on the Ayurdeva plants and herbs and what their purposes are. For any medicinal remedies, an Ayurvedic physician should be consulted for the correct measurements and prescriptions.

Ayurveda and Yoga – This chapter will cover how the sister sciences interact, illustrate basic yoga poses, and inform you of the different types of yoga.

Aromatherapy and Ayurveda - This will be a guide to using fragrant oils for your health, meditations, and beauty.

Ayurvedic Meditation - A guide to meditation, mantras, and sounds for healing. The chapter will also focus on the balancing of emotions and the mind, mantras, healing sounds, and daily routines.

Ayurveda and Beauty - Ayurveda Beauty tips. Ayurveda has so many wonderful beauty tips that will make you feel incredible.

Ayurveda Recipes and Beverages - Recipes and beverages specifically for your Dosha to balance your body.

This is not the kind of book that should be read cover to cover. Instead, it is a guide for you to refer to in order to learn and truly understand what Ayurveda is and what it can be for you in your life.

Ayurveda is all-encompassing—a mind, body, and spiritual awakening. You are a whole person, and this book is designed to show you how to care for yourself and be healthier and calmer, to be able to handle the daily ups and downs of daily life. If you are ready for a true change that will bring health and balance to your life, then read on and learn how the feeling of *Shavasana* can be yours.

Chapter 2: Ayurveda Medicine – What it is, How Safe, and How Effective

What is Ayurvedic Medicine?

Ayurveda, the ancient Indian medical system, is composed of ancient writings that depend on a holistic and natural approach to mental and physical health. It is the oldest medical system and is still one of India's traditional systems for health care. The treatment is a combination of lifestyle, diet, exercise, and products, (mainly originating from plants, but it may also include metal, minerals, and animals). The medicine of Ayurveda is centered on three doshas: Vata, Pitta, and Kapha. Disease begins when the energies of these three doshas are imbalanced.

How much is known about Ayurvedic medicine?

There have only been a few clinical trials using the Ayurvedic approaches, although Ayurvedic medicine and its elements have been defined in many scholarly articles and published in Western medical journals. Currently, 240,000 American adults use Ayurvedic medicine. (NCCIH - National Center for Complementary and Integrative Health, 2019)

Is Ayurvedic medicine safe?

Some Ayurvedic medicines contain herbs, minerals, and metals or other materials. These can be harmful if not used correctly. As is the case of Western medicines that can cause serious side effects, Ayurvedic medicines must be administered with guidance by an Ayurvedic practitioner. (Hopkins, John Medicine, 2019)

Are there any steroids in Ayurvedic medicines?

There are never any synthetic steroids in Ayurvedic medicines. These medicines are made with herbs and plant parts that naturally contain phytosterols, which are natural steroids that are also contained in our foods.

The main objective of Ayurveda and its medicine is to promote longevity, a balanced and healthy life, and forego the necessity of complicated surgeries, prescribed medications, or being distressed from painful ailments.

Ayurveda has had a major resurgence worldwide. In India, people depend on age-old practices that heal health issues, from impotence to intestinal issues. However, as alternative health and complementary practices are now much more popular, Ayurveda is still practiced successfully today.

The medicine practiced by Ayurvedic doctors aids in treating inflammatory issues, digestive issues, an attack on the immune system, and the imbalance of hormones.

Alzheimer's, depression, anxiety, cancer, respiratory diseases, mental diseases, diseases of the brain, high blood pressure, Parkinson's disease, herpes, dysmenorrhea (painful menstruation), PMS (premenstrual syndrome), and cramps can all be helped by Ayurvedic medicine.

Practitioners of Ayurveda employ a diet that is balanced, healthy, aids in stress relief, has transitions in lifestyle, and includes numerous herbal cures that heal and bring the body to balance.

Disease and suffering come from the energy types, or doshas being imbalanced.

In Ayurvedic medicine, all of us are unique in our balance of the three types of energy. We all have some of the three energies embedded in our personalities, yet there is a combination of them and one that is the most dominant. The dominant one eventually rules the level of energy, dispositions, appetite, and propensities. Individually, the doshas have both emotional and physical characteristics. We are using the doshas to describe behaviors that are common of one's personality and physique.

Not like the cookie-cutter practices of medical treatments of the west, which do not attend to the enormous variety of the patients they treat, Ayurvedic medicine considers individuality when prescribing holistic treatments. (Axe, Dr., 2019)

Ayurvedic Medicine – The Three Doshas

Vata

The energy of Vata is customarily thought similar to the wind. This dosha mainly controls movement, flow and circulation, mobility, the ability to breathe, and body functions that are fundamental to live. People whose dominant type is Vata lean towards being energetic and imaginative, but are stressed, fearful, and demonstrate being absent-minded when imbalanced. Vatas usually have small bones, slightly thinner than others, and cannot gain weight very easily. Cold is a sensation they feel most of the time, and they tend to have dry, sensitive skin and a sensitive digestive system.

Pitta

Pitta has an energy-governing metabolism. It incorporates the ingestion of nutrients, the temperature of the body, digestion, and the outflow of energy. People whose dominant type is Pitta are inclined to be intelligent, driven, industrious, and, when their energies are balanced, competitive. When they are imbalanced, they tend to demonstrate extreme anger and aggressiveness. They are medium in physical build, sports-minded, and flexible in weight or muscle gain.

Kapha

The energy of Kapha is thought to be the nourishing dosha and controls growth in the body. It helps to keep a robust immune system and supplies moisture to the organs and cells. When balanced, Kaphas are grounded, loving, supportive, and forgiving. When imbalanced, they can be insecure, lazy, envious, and sad.

By balancing the three doshas and not allowing one dosha to become more dominant while ignoring another, following a healthy diet, handling stress, maintaining relationships, and dealing with change are expected to be easier.

There are two significant characteristics of renewing a balance: connecting into the customary tempos of the body and syncing our way of life with the environment and recurring configurations. This comprises the aligning of food choices, level of activity, the pattern of sleep, and all other facets with each season, hours of the day, and the cycles of menstruation for women. Ayurveda revitalizes a healthy circadian rhythm and helps ease stress in this way. This will benefit everything from your appetite to hormones.

A practitioner of Ayurveda obtains your health history, examines the skin, looks at the gums as well as the tongue, checks the pulse and reflexes, speaks about relationships and how one sleeps, then will prescribe a certain diet and help rebalance your doshas. All these factors assist in determining a dominant dosha and work to find the characteristics that may be imbalanced. An example is if a person is not getting enough sleep, stressed and overworking or not eating enough nutrients. (Axe, Dr., 2019)

Ayurvedic Medicine and its Benefits

Reduced Anxiety and pressure from stress – Stress can be connected to almost all facets of our health. A number of various techniques that address symptoms of depression, stress, and anxiety, reduce cortisol, and bring balance to the hormonal structure of the body, may be used by a practitioner of Ayurvedic medicine. The techniques consist of the practice of yoga, breathing exercises, meditation, the brushing of the skin, herbal treatments, exercises in visualization, or the repetition of mantras.

It has been discovered through various studies that the practice of transcendental meditation, known as Maharishi and an arm of Ayurveda, reduces anxiety through continued habit. Also, sequences of different exercises in breathing, Pranayama, similarly helps in having better energy, calming the nerves, improving hormonal function, and bringing about more restful sleep. Also, while yoga may not always be included in an individual's recovery plan, it can offer well-known benefits for reducing the pressure of stress.

Yoga is an effective, inexpensive choice for people to practice. Attempts are being made to unearth a therapy that is non-pharmacologic to ease pain, anxiety, and stress over several decades. It was found that after reviewing over 35 trials performed in Massachusetts by the St. Elizabeth's Medical Center that tracked yoga and its effects, the findings in 25 of the trials displayed a marked improvement in the indications of anxiety and stress. Also, of the 35 findings, fourteen reported improvements in the biological markers of anxiety as well as stress. It has also been found that people diagnosed with cancer can effectually combat the damage of free radicals and benefit physically by practicing yoga.

Blood Pressure and Cholesterol can be Lowered – Studies have indicated that Ayurveda relaxation techniques and diet can lessen inflammation and aid in the reduction of plaque buildup, as well as reverse atherosclerosis, a disease where fats from cholesterol and various matter form in the internal artery. Substances build up in the inner lining of an artery, which can create a heart attack or stroke. The techniques of Ayurveda can naturally lessen blood pressure and cholesterol.

Recuperation from Ailments – There is research that supports the healing concepts of Ayurveda. Focusing on the cause of diseases, which is inflammation, Ayurvedic treatments can improve blood flow, lessen swelling and pain, fight arthritis, fibromyalgia, and severe inflammatory conditions, as well as prescribe drugs and medications.

A study issued in 2011 discovered a comparison of prescribed medications, known as MTX (methotrexate), with a treatment of Ayurvedic medicine in a random trial that was dually-blind. Every group involved in the 36-week study were similar at curative indicators of adult rheumatoid arthritis. Also, unpleasant effects were fewer in the groups that were assigned to the group only using the Ayurvedic treatment. This group had experienced substantial progress with their symptoms with no adverse results or effects.

Ayurveda is particularly beneficial in detoxification. This is achieved by the use of several herbs, eating healthily, drinking teas, and getting sufficient rest. Also, specified practices boost liver function as well as circulation. This can be achieved by *Abhyanga,* the application of herbs or oils to the body and rubbing them in to amplify circulation and pull toxins from the body. Another practice that might be recommended is the use of different herbs that reduce cortisol like holy basil.

Antioxidant Enriched Diet – Ayurveda supports a diet that is plant-based with a diverse array of wholesome foods. While the diets rest on their needs, the diets for the different body types are all comprised of vegetables, protein, teas, and foods that are high in antioxidant content.

Guidelines for the Ayurvedic diets emphasize eating hot, wholesome foods that are easily digested at the same time as considering a number of variants that rest on someone's ancestry, traditions, and customs. As an example, a practitioner will put thought into the geographic, social, and variables of climates when recommending a balanced diet for each body type.

Detoxifying and the cooling of foods that are fermented is a common practice in coastal areas. Pro-biotic foods are recommended to aid temperature regulation as well as digestion. In other parts of the country, and at colder times of the year, hot and fatty foods that are healthy are emphasized to promote better circulation as well as warm the body.

Helps with Weight Reduction and Maintenance – The primary goal of Ayurvedic medicine is not its most important goal but practicing Ayurveda can aid in the loss of weight by eating healthy foods, lessening the pressure of stress and anxiety, and using oils for weight loss that is natural and not induced by pills or chemicals. A 2009 study showed that changing one's healthy diet focusing on one's food needs and preferences gave help to those who participated in losing weight effectively. This outcome is probably due to Ayurveda supporting a diet that should be realistic, easily followed, and promotes balance.

There were 200 people involved in the study: people that were vatta and had lean body types accounted for 27 percent, people who had medium body types were pitta at 41.5 percent, and larger body kapha types were at 31 percent. At the start of the study, the pitta and kapha people were heavier than the vattas. Three months after following the prescribed programs, the pitta group lost the most weight. The total measurements that were reduced were higher in kapha and pitta people than in the vatta individuals. The diets were based on Ayurvedic constitution and showed supportive weight loss for those who needed to lose the weight. (Axe, Dr., 2019)

Lowers Inflammation – The Ayurvedic medicine theory is a mixture of bad digestion, an unhealthy diet, a lack of sufficient sleep, and inadequate air inhaled, which is the cause of inflammation and oxidative stress resulting in metabolism imbalance.

Healing using Ayurveda focuses on looking at several ways of lessening inflammation with expectations of adjusting and normalizing the heart and circulation, digestion, and method of eliminating the body's waste. By taking care of many issues, plus a person's food intolerances, stress, deficiency of nutrients, and overstimulation, people feel reduced inflammation and greater healing and energy. (Axe, Dr., 2019)

Researchers discovered one of the benefits of Ayurveda, which was the conviction that a single herb or drug cannot treat or heal the imbalance for all. Practitioners usually advise a mixture of staple foods as well as various herbs and plants to treat various inflammatory ailments. An example is the herbal formulation of the benefits of combining turmeric with black pepper, an ancient anti-inflammation recommendation.

Studies have found this mixture of turmeric and black pepper combined increases the speed of healing and reduces toxicity. It is now discovered that curcumin, which is the active ingredient of turmeric, is increased by the active component piperine, found in black pepper, by preventing the glucuronidation of the curcumin. (Axe, Dr., 2019)

Hormonal Balance – For thousands of years, people used Ayurveda to acquire hormonal balance, conceive naturally, and have a healthy menstrual cycle or pregnancy. During the reproductive age in women, the treatment of Polycystic Ovarian Syndrome (PCOS), which is a common endocrine disorder that results from resistance to insulin and the imbalance of hormones, has shown that a number of Ayurvedic healing effects are effective in aiding in the treatment to subfertility. This has been shown in studies about this issue.

It has been discovered that the use of varied essential oils to balance herbal treatments, hormones, and changes in one's routines, for a six month period and daily, was studied and the results were that the majority of the women who participated in the study were successful in being cured of **PCOS**, and with 75 percent of the women conceiving naturally.

Additionally, women who had absent or irregular periods, as well as menstruation or ovulation infrequency, multiple immature follicles, body hair growth and excessive facial hair (that is due to the upsurge of male hormones), thinned hair, and **PMS** symptoms (including oily skin and acne) have all been helped by Ayurveda treatments.

Discover Your Dosha – Take the Dosha Questionnaire

The Dosha questionnaire determines which dosha is your most prominent energy. We are all a combination of the three doshas, but one will emerge to be the most dominant type. It gives an Ayurvedic breakdown of your mind-body type to augment your health and wellbeing.

DOSHA QUESTIONNAIRE

KEY:

5 - Is most like me

3 - Is almost like me

1 - Is rarely like me

Example:

Vata - 3

Pitta - 5

Kapha - 1

Total = 9

CHARACTERISTICS	VATA	PITTA	KAPHA	TOTAL
FRAME	I am thin, lanky, and slender. I have thin muscles	I am a medium build with muscle development	I have a large, stocky or round build and a broad or thick frame	
WEIGHT	I may forget to eat or tend to lose weight - Low	I easily gain or lose weight if I focus on doing so	I gain weight very easily and have a hard time losing it	
EYES	My eyes are active and small	My eyes give a penetrating gaze	My eyes are large and warm	
COMPLEXION	My skin is dry, thin or rough	My skin has a reddish color and is easily irritated	My skin is moist, thick, and smooth	
HAIR	My hair is frizzy or brittle and dry	My hair is fine and is thinning or graying early	My hair is thick, abundant, and oily	
JOINTS	I have joints that are prominent and thin, and they sometimes crack	I have joints that are flexible and fluid	I have joints that are well-knit, large and padded	

SLEEP	Light sleeper who wakes up easily	Moderately sound sleeper and to feel rested need less than eight hours	Sleep long and deep and slowly awaken in the morning
BODY TEMPERATURE	I like warm environments – my hands and feet are usually cold	I like cooler environments – I am usually warm no matter the season	I can adapt to most temperatures but don't like wet, cold days
TEMPERAMENT	I like change, and my nature is enthusiastic and lively	I like to convince, am purposeful, and intense	I like to support, am accepting, and easygoing
UNDER STRESS	I become worried and/or anxious	I become aggressive and/or irritable	I become reclusive and/or remote
TOTAL	_____Vata Total	___Pitta Total	____Kapha Total

The total for each characteristic is 9. Place the highest number 5 in the box that is most like you and the lowest number 1 in the box that least describes you. In the remaining box that somewhat describes you, you place the number 3. The dosha that gets the highest number is your dominant dosha.

When you determine your dominant dosha, you can adjust all the Ayurvedic elements according to your body type. This will bring your body to a better balance. With a more specified diet, the ability to reduce your stress level, and exercise with yoga and other activities that you incorporate, it is possible to lose weight.

Ayurveda does not just rejuvenate and renew, but when you adopt the practice, it opens up an entire lifestyle that will bring you health, calm, peace, and balance.

Chapter 3: Ayurvedic Lifestyle

Ayurveda is more than just attending a yoga class, meditating, or using aromatic oils on occasion. It is all of these and more. Ayurveda is a lifestyle. It is all of these things, seriously incorporated in your life. The blend of mind-body-spirit as a balanced oneness within us is what practicing Ayurveda is really about.

This chapter will cover many facets of how incorporating Ayurveda into your life will bring about balance and change.

Yet, there are some myths and misconceptions about Ayurveda and Ayurvedic medicine that have shrouded this practice in mystery, myths, and misleading untruths. Let's address the misconceptions and myths most often applied to Ayurveda. Learning about them and dispelling any doubts one may have is the best way to have a clear and informed approach to the practice of Ayurveda.

Ayurveda is a system that is obsolete and outdated – The idea that Ayurveda is obsolete and outdated seems to come from the minds of the uninformed and/or the younger generation. For the past 5,000 years, Ayurveda has been in existence and is continued to be practiced today because of its usefulness. Had Ayurvedic medicine not been found effective, this system would not have lasted. It is a form of medicine that is well recorded. Researches and clinical trials were done using Ayurvedic remedies. Diseases were diagnosed, and data about herbs, minerals, and foods were thoroughly recorded and detailed. One of the earliest surgeons in the world, Sushrata, the ancient Indian physician, was well known and practiced Ayurvedic medicine in 600 BCE.

The practice of Ayurveda declined around 1200 CE to 1800 CE. The reason for its decline was due to Afghans invading India and then later on taken over by the British who banished the practice of Ayurveda and forced the use of Western medicine instead.

Today, with the increase of holistic lifestyles, natural, healthy eating, and awakened spirituality, Ayurveda has emerged in its popularity worldwide. (Allayurveda, 2016)

The treatments and remedies of Ayurveda are harmless – When the prescribed and correct dosages of Ayurvedic medicine is taken, the medicines are harmless. However, when the wrong dosage of treatment or the combination of an incorrect dosage is ingested, problems may occur. As an example, the medications using guggul, a herbal preparation used to aid in lowering serum cholesterol, can bring on acidity, especially if it is taken on an empty stomach. It is recommended to take such treatments only after eating and with milk. As with any medicine, any Ayurvedic drugs and treatments should be used with the supervision of an Ayurvedic doctor who is qualified to prescribe them. (Allayurveda, 2016)

Doctors that practice Ayurvedic medicine are not qualified – Doctors practicing Ayurvedic medicine have to have formal degrees before they can begin to practice. The doctors spend four and a half years of disciplined and intense training to earn the Ayurveda BAMS degree in the eight branches of Ayurveda.

After completing their studies, hopeful practitioners are required to complete an obligatory internship for one year. They can then continue to take their post-graduate courses to major in each branch if they choose to do so. (Allayurveda, 2016)

The eight branches of Ayurveda are:

Internal Medicine	Kayachikitsa
Diseases above the shoulder	Shalakya
Surgery	Shalyachikitsa
Psychiatry	Bhutavidya
Toxicology	Agadatantram
Rejuvenation	Rasayanam
Pediatrics	Kaumarabhrutyam
Aphrodisiacs	Vajikaranam

Ayurveda is not an authentic or legitimate science – Ayurveda is a science grounded on natural remedies and herbal preparations. The elements of nature constitute our body, and when any of these elements in our physical body is increased or reduced, it leads to the materialization of various illnesses. This is what Ayurveda believes, and when the health is restored, it is the balance to the elements in the body that Ayurveda addresses.

The treatments of Ayurvedic medicine are not effective – Some Ayurvedic treatments show their effects very quickly, while other medicines and treatments steadily act, but results come more slowly. These types of treatment ensure that the organs and tissues of the body are not damaged while in the process of remedying or terminating disease. The root cause of the disease is released slowly from the body thoroughly, unlike many Western pathological treatments that treat the symptoms rather than the root of the illness, and in the process cause side effects that may be more damaging and harmful to other parts of the body than the illness itself. This is a myth that usually comes up when a person views that treatments are taking longer than they expect. (Allayurveda, 2016)

Ayurveda can't be used for all types of illnesses - The earlier a disease is detected, the quicker and easier the treatment is. All medicinal systems can treat and cure diseases that are caught as early as possible.

Ayurveda can treat certain types of serious illnesses, such as Parkinson's and diabetes, as well as a common cold. People look to Ayurvedic treatment after going the conventional medicinal route—using drugs that may have opposite effects of the symptoms. When people seek Ayurvedic treatment, the illness has progressed to an advanced stage or complications may have developed so it would naturally take a longer period for Ayurvedic treatment to show positive signs that the illness is cured.

Ayurveda only uses herbs - Ayurveda integrates herbs with such items as honey, milk, butter, ghee (clarified butter), salt, and minerals in many of its cures. Not all remedies or herbal products are Ayurvedic. Also, Ayurveda gives yoga exercises and massage (abhyanga) as prescriptions combined with medicinal treatments.

Ayurveda is difficult, expensive, and time-consuming - Ayurveda is none of the above. If you are thinking that taking a yoga class is difficult and expensive, it isn't. If you can stretch, you can do yoga. There are many forms of yoga, and some are gentle like Hatha Yoga—just one of the forms of yoga that are considered good for beginners. You may want to take a few classes to get the best instruction about your poses and get comfortable with the feeling and doing of the exercise. You can then purchase one or two yoga DVDs to practice at home.

Purchasing one or two yoga DVDs eliminates all three arguments—there are forms of yoga on them that are not difficult to perform, and practicing yoga at home eliminates the cost of classes and can be done at your convenience so that you can fit it into your schedule.

It's all about Spa and Massage - Ayurveda is not just about this; it is the practice of syncing the mind, body, and spirit.

Knowing what your Dosha is and how it is best fed, practicing yoga, getting a massage, meditating and using aromatherapy are all the ways that take care of your mind, body, and spirit, and bringing the balance that is the goal of practicing Ayurveda.

We are not perfect beings, and being in perfect balance is something that is strived for in Ayurveda. It helps us to face the world each day and is a way to love ourselves. When we do that, we not only benefit, but everyone around us benefits as well.

It's only for Vegetarians – Ayurveda is not against non-vegetarian food. In some cases, medicines are made from meat. Although it does not advocate meat, Ayurvedic ideologies are applied and the meats, if necessary, can be used to rebuild health according to their benefits and properties to the human body. (Panse, Dr. Rupali, 2018)

Ayurveda has categorized all of the eatable things on Earth comprehensively compared to how other sciences could have classified them. There is a huge categorization of animals, reptiles, birds, aquatic animals, etc., and to the tiniest detail of these animals, from fish to peacock to rhino to rabbit, is the reach of the categorization.

In other words, Ayurveda has classified every form of life that is edible and all its properties. This includes fish, chicken, pork, beef, and all other types of meats. It is recommended that care is taken as to how the meat is prepared. There is more about this topic in Chapter 4 that covers the Ayurvedic foods and diet.

Improve Your Health with Ayurvedic Practices

Many Ayurvedic practices help balance your dosha. Eating a diet that is balanced and partnered with a daily exercise routine is crucial to maintaining a healthy body and mind. The ancient teachings of Ayurveda also have some other practices that can help with weight loss, detoxification, and the improvement of your mind, body, and spirit connection.

Meditation - Meditation can include being aware of your breathing, to moving meditation or yoga. More information on meditation will be covered in Chapter 8.

Breathing exercises (Pranayama) - To clear the lungs of carbon dioxide and increase oxygen intake, deep diaphragmatic breathing provides the body with more fundamental energy. To massage your internal organs and promote digestion, deep belly breathing stimulates metabolism and supports peristalsis, the constriction and relaxation of the intestinal muscles.

A breathing technique that you can try to perform is Kapalabhati, using your abdominal muscles to pull your stomach in and then do a forceful exhalation. This can increase the strength of the digestive fire or Agni and can also give your abdomen a workout.

The Practice of Sweating or Swedana - Your skin is the greatest organ of detoxification. Sweating helps in increasing circulation and rids the body of excess water weight. The pores are open to the heat and become enlarged, allowing the sweat glands to release impurities from the body.

The blissful Ayurvedic spa treatment is called Swedana. The treatment also includes a full-body oil massage followed by steam. The toxins in your body are mobilized, then released through your pores. (O'Connor, 2018)

Make lunchtime your largest meal - The belief that Ayurveda teaches is the digestive fire reaches its peak when the sun reaches its highest point, approximately from 12 noon to 1 p.m. This doesn't mean you consume everything you can, but eating a lighter, smaller breakfast and dinner is digested easier.

Refrain from eating while feeling emotional - If you are absorbed by feelings that make you feel emotional, it is probable that you're distracted and not really seeing or paying attention to what you're eating. At times like these, you may be apt to make poor meal choices, overeat, feel dissatisfaction after a meal, and suffer from poor digestion. Give some time for these feelings to subside before eating a meal.

Breathing deeply and imagining that every time you exhale, you are releasing the emotional feelings and letting them pass, will help you to feel more centered and clearer. Continue and repeat until the feelings pass. Then enjoy a meal.

Don't rush eating your meals - The first step in the process of digesting food is chewing. The digestive enzymes produced by your saliva glands aid in breaking the food down as you chew. Chewing slowly and for longer periods gives your stomach time to send a signal to your brain, telling it you're full. This helps in the prevention of overeating. Try chewing your food until it is almost liquefied before swallowing.

Eat Meals in Silence - This is not to say that you should eat every meal quietly without conversation, but occasionally try eating in silence. You will find that you appreciate your meal and savor the food more, and you'll be attentive to when your body signals you've had enough to eat and are full. This prevents eating more than necessary. (O'Connor, 2018)

Warm Water and Ginger Tea - Drinking water that is cold can hinder the functions of the digestive system. Drinking a sufficient amount of water that is warm or hot and ginger tea over the day, as well as with meals, will aid with digestion.

Laughing Out Loud

Studies from the Mayo Clinic say that when you laugh, the blood circulation is stimulated, endorphins are released, and it promotes relaxation. Have a really good laugh—watch a comedy special or movie, tell jokes, read a funny article, and laugh at yourself too.

Benefits of Practicing Ayurveda – Yoga And Meditation

People around the world practice Ayurveda by incorporating many of its aspects into their lives. Many practice for different reasons—to be one with their faith with yoga, to escape the frenetic world that is their ever-busy, all-encompassing life or dealing with the grief of losing a loved one. People find a space to be calm when they practice yoga or meditate.

Millions of unknown and many well-known people meditate, use the practice of yoga, and another form of Ayurveda. Here are a few celebrities who have made meditation and yoga a part of their daily lives:

Christy Turlington Burns, one of the top supermodels of the 90s and now a documentary filmmaker, began practicing yoga at the age of eighteen and then was introduced to other facets of Ayurveda to find her balance. She began her modeling career at fourteen years of age working after school and during her summer vacations. She moved to New York City after turning eighteen to model full time and graduate from high school.

Turlington continues her practice of yoga, in particular, a type of yoga known as Jivamukti, an ethical, physical, and spiritual practice. She practices three times a week in the morning and credits the practice with easing the pain of natural childbirth and the closeness she feels to her Catholic faith.

Turlington has authored the book *Living Yoga: Creating a Life Practice.* (Omblabla, 2018)

Novak Djokovic may not be a name familiar to some, but those who play tennis or are enthusiastic spectators, know the professional tennis player well. Originally from Serbia, Djokovic is currently ranked world No.1 in men's singles tennis per the Association of Tennis Professionals (ATP). (Wikipedia, 2019)

Djokovic is well aware of the pressures of not being at the top of his game, and every time he competes, having the ability and talent to remain at the top. There is an enormous amount of stress and pressure, so Djokovic meditates to bring it all down a few notches. "You need to have a quiet place where you can switch off and recharge your batteries. I can just say that it's... very calm and very beautiful... where I like to spend time." Novak Djokovic (Singh, 2017)

Oprah Winfrey has worn many hats in her lifetime. She began her career in television, first as an on-air news anchor, then hosted and produced her own talk show. She has acted in and produced many award-winning films, been a television producer for the programs *Dr. Phil, Rachel Ray,* and *Dr. Oz,* and is a philanthropist, known for her generosity to many organizations and the establishment of the Oprah Winfrey Leadership Academy for Girls in Henley on Klip, South Africa. Winfrey has also joined with Deepak Chopra to sponsor the 21 Day Meditation Challenge Day.

Winfrey, whose dosha is Kapha, allows herself a good amount of quiet time at least once or twice a day. She meditates for twenty minutes in the morning and twenty minutes again in the evening. Winfrey believes that all her peace and creative expression comes from her daily meditations. The practice has been a help in connecting to her spiritual center and understanding her moment of destiny. Winfrey introduced meditation to her Harpo Studios staff. Each morning at 9 a.m. and each afternoon at 4:30 p.m., the company stops and meditates. In her extremely busy day, she finds the experience of calmness from the quiet space of meditation that can help create the best work and life. (Singh, 2017) (Dyson, Tracy, 2015)

Robert Downey, Jr. is a man who has come back from crippling addictions with the help of yoga. He works with one of Los Angeles' well-known yogis, Vinnie Marino. Downey practices Power Flow yoga and feels that every session gives him a feeling of being reflective and calm. He has found his spiritual balance in yoga.

Michelle Williams not only practices yoga but also co-founded The Yoga for Single Moms Project. The project provides a location for women to attend a yoga class and has separate day care for the kids. Williams turned to meditation and yoga for spiritual help following the death of her ex-partner, Heath Ledger, the father of their daughter, Matilda. (Do You Yoga, 2019)

Russell Brand is another man of the triple addictions of drugs, sex, and alcohol that became part of his life after he reached stardom. Now sober from all his addictions, he finds meditation to be the tool to find a state of deeper happiness and keep him sober. Today, Brand teaches a Kundalini yoga class and has other celebrities join him—for instance, Rumer Willis and her mom, Demi Moore. (Dyson, Tracy, 2015)

Tina Turner has always credited her practice of meditation for helping her have the strength to leave her abusive marriage with Ike Turner. Her life after she left him was somewhat of a financial struggle after she assumed responsibility for the contractual breach of contract incurred by the cancellation of their tour as well as a lien against them from the IRS.

Turner has remarried now and resides in Switzerland. She continues to meditate daily and has recorded albums dedicated to prayers and chants that are based on her practice of meditation. (Dyson, Tracy, 2015)

Orlando Bloom, who is a Vata dosha, meditates daily to help him keep away from the paths in Hollywood that can be destructive. Thus far he's been very successful in side-stepping the many temptations that exist in Hollywood. Bloom meditates to find strength and peace. (Dyson, Tracy, 2015)

Katy Perry turned to yoga and meditation to deal with the breakup of her marriage to Russell Brand. A few months after concluding their divorce, Perry joined a meditation group and said it changed her life. Perry continues to practice yoga and meditates daily. (Do You Yoga, 2019)

Ayuveda is the oldest medical system, yet it has had many myths and misconceptions. However, it is an actual science; the physicians who practice Ayurvedic medicine are well trained, as are physicians who practice Western medicine.

Millions of people around the world practice Ayurveda for many different reasons. Some practice by meditating and doing yoga to find peace from a hectic and demanding career, or to find solace from the grief they endure because of the loss of a loved one or a relationship. Others practice for their health, all practice for their wellbeing.

Ayurveda is about the balance of the mind, body, and spirit. It is about how the body is fed and treated and how yoga and meditation care for the mind and spirit. When you practice Ayurveda, you are doing what is best for your entire being. Begin to follow and understand the tenets that you have learned in this chapter, and you will begin to notice the positive changes that come with the practice of Ayurveda.

Chapter 4: Ayurvedic Diet – What to Eat and the Effects of an Ayurvedic Diet

The Ayurvedic diet is a wellness system that dates back thousands of years. The diet and its lifestyle practices can help improve one's health. The diet is a plan/guide for the food you eat and how to avoid or manage illness, improve your health, and maintain your wellbeing. If you eat following an Ayurvedic diet, you will primarily consume whole fresh foods or foods that are minimally processed, and you will practice eating rituals.

The Principles of Ayurvedic Eating

You will integrate many different routines into your eating program if you follow an Ayurvedic diet. Some eating practices include:

Six tastes or rasas - For each meal, you will incorporate foods that are sweet, salty, sour, bitter, and pungent. You will begin your meal with the sweet taste of a fruit, then eat salty food like seafood, and sour, citrus fruit like an orange. To finish the meal, you'll eat foods like peppers or onions that are pungent and astringent like green apples or tea, and finally green leafy vegetables for the bitter portion of the meal.

o *Concentrate on eating.* Avoid distractions like talking or laughing. Focus on your meal to fully appreciate it and the benefits you are deriving from the meal.

o *Savor the taste of the food and eat slowly.*

o *Don't allow hot food to get cold.* Eat quickly enough to avoid that from happening, but not too quick in that you would get indigestion.

o *Pay attention to your hunger signals, so you don't overeat.* Eat the right amount of food.

o *Only eat when the meat you previously ate has digested.* Ayurvedic guidelines recommend no eating within three hours of your last snack or meal and not to go without eating for more than six hours. Also, practitioners suggest eating a light breakfast and having a large and satisfying lunch. You may eat dinner or perhaps not based on your hunger level. (Frey, 2018)

You are eating according to your dominant dosha. The main point of following this diet is that you eat the diet that is recommended for your dosha. Your dominant dosha is your predominant energy. Doshas in Ayurveda are derived from five elements: space, air, water, fire, and earth, providing various characteristics:

o **Vata/air and space** – Vatas are defined as intense and creative. The properties include light, dry, rough, and cold.

o **Pita/fire and water** – Pittas are defined as joyful, smart, and driven. Properties include hot, sharp, mobile, and liquid.

o **Kapha/earth and water** – Kaphas are defined as loving, tranquil, or sluggish. Properties include dense, yielding, moist, and unchanging.

After you read the definitions of the doshas, you could feel that one dosha is more like the attributes you symbolize. Many times, people discover they have almost equally strong doshas. Practitioners of the Ayurvedic lifestyle feel that we each embody all three doshas. The prominent dosha is the one that determines what and how you eat. (Frey, 2018)

Beginning to Eat According to Your Dosha

Before you begin an Ayurvedic diet, it could be a good idea to spend time finding and learning about your dominant dosha. There are several ways to do this:

Locate an Ayurvedic Doctor

The best way to start your diet, experts suggest, is to visit an Ayurvedic physician. Although there are different ways to find your dosha, an Ayurvedic physician will help determine the best choice of herbs and foods and address any medical concerns that you may want to focus on. The right mix of foods for your dosha to be balanced will allow the diet to be more effective.

Remember, an Ayurvedic physician residing in the United States may not be a licensed medical doctor. Most Ayurvedic physicians have earned their degrees in naturopathic medicine in India. There are a few schools of Ayurveda, according to the National Institutes of Health (NIH).

The NIH gives guidance for choosing a complementary care provider. It is additionally recommended that you speak with your healthcare professional regarding using Ayurveda as a health practice.

If you can meet with an Ayurvedic physician, they will assess what your dosha is based on the interview and the information that you provide. This is probably the best and most precise way of finding your dosha.

Finding Your Dosha Online

There are numerous online websites with questionnaires that help you discover your dosha. However, questionnaires may not always reflect accuracy.

A study discovered that questionnaires that were administered to find a person's dosha type yielded outcomes that were inconsistent and varied. The researchers wrote, "It is probable that results for three doshas at the same time for the same subject under the same conditions may be different." (Frey, 2018)

Thus, finding your dosha is subjective and not founded on objective data like a urine or blood test. If you see an Ayurvedic physician, though, it may turn out to be exact.

What does this mean? This means that you are probably going to find that your dosha is a combination of more than one type, which is not unusual. We are a combination of different DNA, so it is no surprise that our dosha is a combination as well. You may find the need for some adjusting to find your balance.

Eating the Right Foods for Your Dosha

Once you have found your predominant dosha, you can create meals with the foods that balance your energy and nourish your body. There are more extensive guides for eating based on your dosha type on websites. One website is The Ayurveda Institute (www.ayurveda.com). You can also look at a few sites of organizations specifically for each dosha.

o **Foods to eat for Vata** – Sweet, cooked cherries and apples; vegetables like beets and asparagus; rice and quinoa; red lentils; eggs; beef and fish; dairy products; coriander leaves; black pepper; vinegar, pecans and peanuts; flax or chia seeds; white wine and beer; glee and sesame oil.

o **Foods to avoid for Vata** – Watermelon and uncooked apples; uncooked, frozen and dried vegetables; barley, chickpeas, split peas, corn, and potatoes; lamb and turkey; yogurt; chocolate; and red wine. (Frey, 2018)

o **Foods to eat for Pitta** - Watermelon and coconut; raisins; bitter or sweet vegetables like cauliflower and broccoli; pasta; dry cereal; unsalted butter; beans; white meat; almonds; egg whites; and white wine and beer.

o **Foods to avoid for Pitta** – Apricots, avocado, raw leeks, spinach, and onions; bread with yeast; butter that's salted; chili pepper; sour cream; soy sauce; dark chicken meat and beef; chocolate; and sweet wine and red wine. (Frey, 2018)

o **Foods to eat for Kapha** – Prunes, celery, and carrots; applesauce; polenta; granola; beans, including lima; cottage cheese; buttermilk; turkey and shrimp; and dry red wine and white wine.

o **Foods to avoid for Kapha** – Figs and grapefruit; juicy and sweet vegetables like zucchini and cucumber; hard or soft cheeses; pasta; pancakes; oats; kidney beans; duck and fish; ketchup; chocolate; and alcohol that is "hard", such as whiskey. (Frey, 2018)

Ayurvedic Diet for Wellness or Weight Loss

There are some concerns to consider if you are contemplating beginning an Ayurveda-based diet for improved health or to lose weight. The primary issue is how effective the diet will be. You want to invest in a plan that is reinforced by evidence. The second to consider is adherence. Adopt an eating plan *only* if you can manage and maintain one over time if you want to lose weight and have beneficial results.

Does Scientific Evidence Support Ayurveda?

Although Ayurveda and its medical system has seen thousands of years of practice, the proof to support the practice to be an effective one has been observed.

As interest increases in Ayurvedic medicine by the Western world, there have been high-quality studies conducted by researchers in favor of using the system for the improvement of health:

o Harvard University researchers did a study that supported the use of interventions of holistic health. They included Ayurveda to aid people to adhere to healthy, new behavior.

o Researchers from Harvard University, the University of Connecticut, and Emory University conducted a pilot investigation and discovered that Ayurvedic practices enhanced health among obese and overweight yoga students. The results, the researchers cautioned, though, should be construed with attention to problems with the design of the study and other matters.

o A study from the University of New Mexico and the University of Arizona saw a yoga-based Ayurvedic program that modified a person's daily life as a feasible and acceptable way of managing one's weight.

o There have also been studies that have verified that Ayurveda helps reduce the risk of coronary disease. It also aids in the duration and quality of sleep and is good for managing type 2 diabetes.

Is it possible to stick to an Ayurvedic diet?

As with any diet, an eating plan does not work if you don't follow the diet and apply it to your daily regimen for a term where you see results. There are increasing reports that there is evidence that supports an Ayurvedic diet for wellness and weight loss can be effective. However, some people have a difficult time managing and continuing to maintain the program because of limited food choices, and the taste of some foods may be hard when they start the diet. But when the benefits of the types of food are understood, the taste ends up not mattering as much.

The taste issue aside, the complex diet could be overwhelming and daunting for some people. If a dosha diet is too complex for you, experts recommend using basic eating principles. Some

Ayurvedic practitioners don't recommend foods specific to your dosha if the diet is too complex but would rather you eat foods that help your digestion. Also, with practices like yoga or meditation, which help you to listen to your body, intuitive exercise, eating, and coming into balance results. Focus on wellness rather than weight loss. Following an Ayurvedic diet is great for getting the healthiest balance and weight size that is specific to your nature or constitution.

There is no cookie-cutter equation. Everything about the Ayurvedic diet is personalized. There is no one-size-fits-all equation. Everything is fitted to an individual's needs, and the diet is a habit for life, not temporary.

Eat nutritious whole foods rather than processed foods, be instinctual about eating, and keep an eye on the size of your portions.

Ayurveda experts recommend eating a light breakfast and eating until you feel full. Don't have another meal until you feel hunger. Also, take a walk after a large meal. If you do get hungry, eat a small meal for dinner. Eating until you feel full gives freedom from the feeling of deprivation and counting calories. (Frey, 2018)

Adopting a lifestyle that is shaped to your needs will get better results without starving or having the feeling that you are trapped in a diet that is unpleasant or restrictive. When the balance of the body and mind takes place, you will thrive.

Millions of people are practicing the Ayurvedic diet, and have been for thousands of years, so it has been accepted as a main factor of whole wellness and health. There are several facets of the eating plan that coincide with the essentials of nutrition promoted by Western health, along with medical experts.

If you want to lose weight, you will see the results you want if you decide that an Ayurvedic diet is right for you and develop your eating and meals around those foods that are unprocessed and wholesome as well as practicing the mindful eating tips that work in conjunction with the foods you eat. (Frey, 2018)

Ayurvedic Weight Loss Meal Plan

Below is an example of what a typical meal should look like. Keep in mind to eat what is appropriate for your dosha:

Breakfast – Easy to digest foods like hot oatmeal, fresh fruit, or warm cereal. Eggs are difficult to digest, so go with egg whites.

Lunch – Can include cheese, eggs, meats, and desserts. The digestive fire is at its most powerful and will assimilate and digest everything around noon. Lunch should be the largest meal of the day.

Dinner – The digestive fire is at its weakest, so a light meal like cooked vegetables or soups is preferred. Undigested food gets converted to toxins, and then it's stored in fat cells. Keep dinner light. (Krishna, BAMS, Arya, 2019)

How to Cut the Belly Fat

We all want to have a flat belly, and Ayurveda has some incredible remedies to cut through the stubborn fat, but it also provides natural ways to reduce weight holistically. (Rana, 2019)

Ayurveda sites a few reasons that we tend to gain weight, such as an unhealthy diet, not exercising, oversleeping, and how we live. These factors link with each other and lead to the accumulation of fat, particularly around the belly area.

According to Ayurveda, obesity is a disorder of metabolism and fat tissue. In this state, fat tissue increases and blocks all the digestive system channels, which continues to lead to gaining weight.

There are a few herbal and natural remedies that may aid in cutting belly fat. Some spices, like ginger and black pepper, can also aid in reducing fat. Drinking warm water improves digestion while drinking cold water makes it difficult to lose weight and reduce fat.

It cannot be stated enough that you must partner these remedies with a healthy diet and an exercise program to ensure weight loss.

Methi (Fenugreek) – Rich in numerous health benefits, fenugreek or methi is known to help lose weight efficiently. Digestion is supported by methi, which is the key to shedding the pounds. Galactomannan is a water-soluble component found in methi that helps curb cravings and keep you feeling fuller longer. Methi also increases your metabolism. All that is needed is to roast methi seeds and crush them with a mortar and pestle until they are a fine powder. Add the powder to water and drink it on an empty stomach first thing in the morning. The seeds can also be soaked in water overnight. Chew the soaked seeds on an empty stomach. (Rana, 2019)

Guggul (Commiphora Mukul) – Guggul has been long used in various Ayurvedic medicines and is a herbal remedy. It contains guggulsterone, a plant sterol that is said to promote weight loss by having the body's metabolism stimulated. It also lowers cholesterol as well. Guggul tea is, in many ways, said to be effective.

Vijaysar (Pterocarpus Marsupium) – Vijaysar is a deciduous tree whose bark is used in a number of Ayurvedic medicines to manage obesity and diabetes. Vijaysar is said to have properties that are fat reducing, and thus assist in shedding stubborn belly fat. Additionally, the resin and bark are used for a healthy digestive system. You can drink a cupful of herbal Vijaysar to get effective results. (Rana, 2019)

Triphala – Triphala helps to rejuvenate the digestive system by eliminating toxins from the body. Triphala is an ancient concoction and made using three dried fruits, haritaki, bibhitaki, and amalaki amla. They all have rejuvenating and cleansing properties. Ayurveda experts recommend drinking hot water with the triphala churna at least two hours after dinner and a half hour before breakfast.

Punarnava (Boerrrhavia Diffusa) - Punarnava is known to be an effective diuretic and good for the weight loss process. Its properties help the urinary bladder and the kidney to have an improved function, which further helps in flushing the toxins from the body without losing essential minerals like electrolytes and potassium. Water retention is also reduced—another factor that can cause weight gain. Another benefit is that it also manages digestive ailments like constipation and helps one lose weight healthily. You can drink punarnava tea and lose weight effectively.

Dalchini (Cinnamon) - Dalchini or cinnamon helps in stimulating the metabolism and further aids in cutting belly fat. It is the cinnamaldehyde in cinnamon that stimulates the metabolism of the visceral tissue—which could also help to cut belly fat. Drink a cupful of cinnamon tea first thing in the morning or as recommended by your doctor.

Results vary from one person to another, so it is advised to speak with an Ayurvedic expert before you add any of the above to your diet and if you want to take them in supplement form. People with diabetes, in particular, need to be aware of the doses. (Rana, 2019)

Furthermore, the NHIC warns that Ayurveda herbs, products, or combinations of herbs, can be harmful if misused. It is wise to speak with your health care provider before you make any changes to your diet or consume herbal medicines. Make sure that the changes do not affect any medications or medical ailments you have.

Chapter 5: Ayurvedic Herbs, Herbal Medicine and Health Benefits

Ayurveda – Herbs and How They Are Used

Ayurvedic herbs are used as a part of the holistic method for health that may involve nutrition, meditation, aromatherapy, yoga, and massage. Ayurvedic practitioners frequently use therapeutic spices and oils along with Ayurvedic herbs to promote wellness and treat illness.

A key component of Ayurveda is Ayurvedic herbs that are used in the traditional practice of medicine in India. These herbs are commonly used to boost defenses against disease, "cleanse" the body and help keep the body, mind, and spirit balanced.

The fundamental principle of Ayurvedic medicine is to treat and prevent illness rather than "react" to disease. This is achieved by the balance between the body, mind, and surroundings. The herbs are seldom used on their own but used as a portion of an approach to health that is holistic. (Wong, 2019)

Herbal Medicine – Why More People Are Using Natural Herbal Treatments

Whether or not it is universally known, or acknowledged, about 25 percent of the prescribed drugs in the world originate from plants. Eleven percent of the 252 drugs that are essential and listed in the World Health Organization are plant-based. Actually, the first pharmacological compound morphine, created 200 years ago, was derived from opium extricated from the poppy seeds in the flower. (Ruggeri CHHC, 2017)

Ever since that time, the study of plants has scientists creating the prescriptions and medical products that we know of today. However, overmedication, treating illness, and facing resistant bacteria in the microbiome (the internal ecosystem of bacteria that is located in our bodies, the majority of them in our digestive system), has seen a turning of attention to natural treatments and herbal medicine.

Recently, there have been millions of dollars invested in a search for promising herbs for medicinal use. In comparison to the overall pharmaceutical industry, these considerable financial investments for researching herbal medicine are not as large as dollars expended on prescription drug research but indicate that researchers are starting to move away from the development of prescribed drugs and towards natural and alternative forms of treatment.

Plants are being used for numerous health conditions and concerns, including arthritis, allergies, fatigue, migraines, wounds, skin infections, gastrointestinal issues, burns, and even cancer—proving the truth that food can be a medicine.

Medicinal herbs are safer, do not incur a large expense, and are a way to be treated other than prescribed medications. Going back to the traditional idea of medicine is why many people are choosing herbal medical treatments. (Ruggeri CHHC, 2017)

Herbal Medicine – What it Is

Herbal medicines are natural plant-originated matter used to treat diseases and ailments in regional or local practices of healing. Mixtures that are complex and made of organic chemicals that could be derived from a processed or raw portion of plants are how the herbal products are made.

In every culture worldwide, herbal medicine has its roots. Traditional medical systems and their practices and philosophy are affected by the environment. Different systems of traditional medicine and the practices and philosophy of each are influenced by the environment, geographical location, and social conditions. However, systems agree to a holistic way of life. Ayurvedic medicine and Traditional Chinese medicine are well-known systems of herbal medicine that hold beliefs in the core concept that there must be an importance placed on the promotion of health rather than the ailment. People can thrive and focus on their total condition by using healing herbs instead of a specific illness that is derived from the imbalance of the mind, body, and environment.

Medicine based on plants continues to be used in modern medicine. It was estimated recently that 80 percent of people around the world depend upon Ayurvedic medicines as a portion of their main health care. Additionally, because of returning interest in organic or natural cures and the rising cost of prescription drug medications, there has been additional interest in herbal medications in the United States.

There are many ingredients that whole herbs have which are used to relieve symptoms and treat illnesses. Botanical or herbal medicine uses a plant's roots, bark, flower, berries, and seed to create a medicine used for treatment. There are many beneficial effects of the biological properties of these plants. The way a plant is grown, the environment where the plant grew, how it has been harvested, and how it's been processed are other factors that are responsible for its benefits.

Plants are either sold as extracts or raw, where they are softened with alcohol, water or other thinners to take out some of the chemicals. Results of this process are products that contain dozens of chemicals, including sterols, alkaloids, fatty acids, glycosides, flavonoids, saponins, and others. (Ruggeri CHHC, 2017)

Herbal Medicine and Its Benefits

Herbal medicines are more affordable – One of the reasons that there is an interest in herbal medicine, and it has become more popular in recent years, is the high price tag of pharmaceuticals. People are unable to pay for expensive medications monthly, not to mention the annual increases in pricing for these pharmaceuticals. (Ruggeri CHHC, 2017)

In a recent evaluation of whether natural herbal products were a less costly choice in treating disease or not, it was found that there was less of a cost.

Herbal medicines are easier to obtain – Herbal extracts, herbal teas, and essential oils are herbal products that are available in health food stores and some grocery stores. There is no need to see a physician to get a prescription before purchase. Thus, it is easier to avoid health care costs and get herbal products.

The classification of herbs is as dietary supplements. This is so they can be marketed and sold without being subjected to the FDA. It is easier for the public to purchase them, but we, as consumers, have to make it our business to choose among all the competitors. Only purchase from trustworthy companies that have a good reputation in verifying that their products are 100 percent pure-grade, and read the ingredients, labels, and directions for dosage. (Ruggeri CHHC, 2017)

Healing properties that are beneficial – Chronic and acute ailments, including health concerns such as a weakened immune system, cardiovascular disease, prostate problems, depression, and inflammation, use herbs for treatment. Herbs are used worldwide to treat diseases, and studies prove their effectiveness. There are currently 177 drugs approved around the world for cancer treatment. 70 percent of these drugs are natural or chemical-based.

Top Ten Herbs for Medicinal Purposes

The following herbs are widely used, can address many conditions, and are extremely cost-efficient compared to prescription drugs. If you are looking to replace or complement a medication with a natural herb product, here is a list of ten of the most used herbs in Ayurvedic medicine. As a reminder, please consult your health care specialist in making any changes or additions to your medical regimen. (Ruggeri CHHC, 2017)

1. Raw Garlic – Flavonoids, selenium, allicin, oligosaccharides, and levels high in sulfur are the vital nutrients contained in garlic. Garlic can be consumed raw, cooked, or by capsule. Garlic can help in the reversal of diabetes, enhance the immune system, control blood pressure, combat inflammation, lessen the effects of allergies, combat cardiovascular disease, fight viruses and fungal infections, and control hair loss.

Research shows a reverse association in eating garlic and advancement of cardiovascular disease. Additionally, garlic can reduce cholesterol, reduce blood pressure, increase antioxidant status, and inhibit platelet clustering based on research published in the *Journal of Nutrition*. (Ruggeri CHHC, 2017)

2. Ginger – This is a widely used condiment worldwide. The benefits derived from ginger are therapeutic and from the oily resin known as gingerols, acquired from ginger's root. It is a powerful anti-inflammatory and antioxidant— properties that control the aging process.

Gingerol relieves nausea, indigestion, increases respiratory and immune function, combats fungal infections, bacterial infections, reduces pain, improves diabetes, treats stomach ulcers, prevents malabsorption (a gastrointestinal disorder), and may hinder the growth of cancer cells.

Ginger can be ingested in supplement or powder form. It can be made into a tea and consumed, applied in oil topically, or eaten raw. (Ruggeri CHHC, 2017)

3. Turmeric – Turmeric is a plant and is historically one of the oldest herbs used, dating back almost 4,000 years. Recognition of the importance of turmeric by modern medicine has begun, as shown by over 3,000 publications dealing with turmeric.

Several studies show that turmeric has antioxidant and anti-inflammatory properties. As an antioxidant, turmeric forages free radicals.

4. Ginseng – This has been used in North America and Asia for centuries and is a very popular herbal medicine worldwide. Native Americans used the root of ginseng as a headache remedy and stimulant. Ginseng reduces stress, treats sexual dysfunction, helps weight loss, improves lung function, boosts the immune system, lowers blood sugar levels, and reduces irritation. Ginseng can be purchased as a tea, dried, a powder, a tablet or in a capsule form. (Ruggeri CHHC, 2017)

5. Milk Thistle – For almost 2,000 years, extracts have been used from milk thistle to act as medicinal curatives. Milk thistle is known to be used as an anti-inflammatory and aids the digestive tract, improves skin health, lowers cholesterol levels, and acts as a detoxifier.

Milk thistle was found to have protective effects in certain types of cancer after clinical trials reviewed evaluations of the safety and effectiveness of the herb. Data has shown it to have been used for diabetes, hepatitis C, liver disease, and HIV. Usually sold in capsules, milk thistle extracts are known to be well-tolerated and safe.

6. Feverfew – A centuries-old herb, feverfew has been used for insect bites, fevers, headaches, toothaches, problematic menstruation, infertility, and labor during childbirth. The herb has a pain-easing effect that comes from parthenolides, a biochemical that combats the swelling and widening of the blood vessels that happens in migraines. Feverfew can lessen the pain of arthritis, avert dizziness, ease allergies, and inhibit blood clots.

Feverfew can be taken as a tablet, capsule, or liquid form. It is possible to use the feverfew leaves and make tea. However, it is said the taste is bitter and possibly irritating to the mouth. (Ruggeri CHHC, 2017)

7. Ginkgo Biloba – Ginkgo Biloba, an ancient plant extract, is also known as maidenhair and used in Traditional Chinese Medicine. It has healed numerous illnesses over thousands of year. Today's research indicates that it is connected in cognitive operation and has positive effects on neurological impairment. Other benefits are improved concentration, improved memory function, a reduction of Alzheimer's disease risk and dementia, maintaining vision and eye health, fighting the symptoms and illnesses of depression, anxiety, and fibromyalgia, and improving the libido.

8. St. John's Wort – This is a medicinal herb known for its anti-inflammatory and antidepressant properties. It's been used for over 2,000 years. The biologically active substances hyperforin and hypericin have the greatest medical activity above the dozens of substances produced by the herb. St. John's wort is used as an antidepressant to improve mood swings during menopause, relieve PMS symptoms, fight inflammation, improve symptoms of obsessive-compulsive disorder, and relieve irritated skin flareups. (Ruggeri CHHC, 2017)

9. Aloe Vera – This is used for skin ailments, constipation, infections, and colic. It is suggested to treat fungal diseases in Chinese medicine and is used in the cosmetic, food, and pharmaceutical industries in the Western world.

Aloe vera is thought of as the most active of all the aloe species; there have been 75 possibly active elements that are identified in the plant. These elements include vitamins, amino acids, minerals, saccharides, enzymes, and many others. Aloe vera provides 90 percent of required amino acids and 100 percent of essential amino acids.

Studies have proved the antibacterial, antiviral, antifungal, and anti-inflammatory elements of aloe vera. It has also been proven to be a good builder of the immune system and is non-allergic.

Other benefits of using aloe vera are the ability to soothe skin irritations, treat cold sores, burns, provide antioxidants, moisturize the hair, scalp, and skin, and lessen inflammation. It can be used topically or orally and is found in health food stores and online. (Ruggeri CHHC, 2017)

10. Saw Palmetto – The saw palmetto supplements are used by men with prostatic hyperplasia and prostate cancer. Saw palmetto is known to aid many common male health problems, such as an enlarged prostate, hair loss, and loss of libido. Saw palmetto is an anti-inflammatory and increases immune function, promotes relaxation, and treats respiratory conditions.

Grow a Dosha Herbal Garden

It is possible to create a garden of herbs on your patio or windowsill. Growing your herbs for dosha-balancing wellness, lets you use them at the peak of their potency—immediately after they are trimmed. There is also a positive effect even before you consume the herbs, especially if you are growing the herbs indoors.

Each plant impacts you differently, from influencing your mood and space to oxygenating the air. (Karras, 2017)

Here are some herbs for each dosha:

Vata – *Lemon Balm, Ginger Root, Chamomile*

Benefits of *Lemon Balm*: Relaxing, relieves bloating, and helps with PMS symptoms

Tips on Gardening: Before it blooms, keep it from outgrowing its container

Benefits of *Ginger Root*: Warming, grounding, and relieves nausea

Tips on Gardening: Plant after roots sprout with store-bought ginger; likes afternoon shade

Benefits of *Chamomile*: Is good for destressing and reduces inflammation

Tips on Gardening: Loves the sun but not heat; bring indoors when the temperature is above 75° (Karras, 2017)

Pitta – *Mint, Rose Petals, Lemongrass*

Benefits of *Mint*: Aids digestion, detoxifying, and cooling

Tips on Gardening: Water well as it loves moisture; just before it flowers, the flavor is the richest

Benefits of *Rose Petals*: Supports circulation, energizing, and an aphrodisiac

Tips on Gardening: Loves the full sun; oils degrade within twelve hours of plucking, so use as soon as possible

Benefits of *Lemongrass*: Aids digestion, cooling

Tips on Gardening: Take grocery-store stems and place them in water; when roots appear, plant in soil (Karras, 2017)

Kapha – *Sage, Holy Basil, Thyme*

Benefits of *Sage*: Aids breathing, detoxifying

Tips on Gardening: Loves dryness; don't overwater and use a pot with good drainage

Benefits of *Holy Basil*: Stimulates the body and mind

Tips on Gardening: When temperatures reach sub 50°, bring indoors; stem/leaves above five inches are the most potent; loves water

Benefits of *Thyme*: Controls bacteria and promotes energy

Tips on Gardening: Loves sun and heat; don't overwater

(Karras, 2017)

A few last words and thoughts about herbal medicine:

o Throughout human history, herbs have been used for many reasons. The history of natural "medicine" dates back to ancient times.

o Herbal medicines come from plants and essences used to treat diseases and conditions within regional or local healing practices.

o Focusing on prevention rather than treating diseases or illnesses once they arise and focusing on overall wellness is what is being noticed about the use of herbal medicine today.

o Herbal medicine is more cost-efficient compared to prescribed medications. Also, there is no problem with purchasing them without a prescription, and they provide numerous benefits for health and wellbeing that can be compared to modern pharmaceuticals.

o Garlic, turmeric, saw palmetto, aloe vera, ginger, and St. John's wort are some of the most popular herbs used in herbal medicinal treatments.

o It's crucial that consumers choose products that are pure and have high-quality consistency. If you plan on taking herbal products over a lengthy period, consult a herbalist or health care professional who can provide direction.

o Allergic reactions may occur with herbal medicines or interacting with conventional drugs. Speak with a health care professional before beginning any herbal treatment. There are several health providers as well as herbalists, medical physicians, and other natural and Ayurvedic practitioners that can make available any information and help in choosing what herbal treatment is the best to treat your health needs and concerns.

o Research herb use and be aware of appropriate dosages and the possibility of side effects.

Chapter 6: Ayurveda and Yoga

Ayurvedic Yoga – What is the Practice of Yoga?

Yoga has been part of the practice of Ayurveda for more than 5,000 years. It can be said that yoga is the ancient and first formalized exercise program to have been developed.

So many benefits are derived from yoga. Not only does it burn calories and tone muscles, but it is also a mind-body workout combining poses that stretch and strengthen with deep breathing and relaxation or meditation. (Watson, n.d.)

Yoga is an important component of safeguarding sound health, according to Ayurveda. Ayurveda and yoga have to do with purifying the bodily and mental faculties, achieving a union with the higher power, God, the divine—whatever you recognize. Yoga is thought to be the exercise arm of Ayurveda.

The great popularity of yoga is when used therapeutically; the potential to manage the stress that permeates the body and the mind with the calm that yoga offers.

Although yoga is not considered an alternative to modern medicine, it can be supportive in the process of healing, particularly diseases that are provoked by stress, such as hypertension, diabetes, and asthma.

Yoga and Health Benefits

Although there are hundreds of different types or schools of yoga, most yoga sessions include meditation, exercises in breathing, and assuming poses, sometimes called asana, that flex and stretch the muscle groups.

The techniques of relaxation that are integrated into yoga can help to address and lessen chronic pain, such as arthritis, pain in the lower back, headaches, and carpal tunnel syndrome. Yoga also helps to reduce insomnia—and any problems that interrupt sleep—and lower blood pressure. (American Osteopathic Association, 2019)

The physical benefits of yoga:

- o Increased muscle tone and strength
- o Improved energy and respiration
- o Increased flexibility
- o Weight reduction
- o Balanced metabolism
- o Improved athletic performance
- o Circulatory and cardio health
- o Protection from injury

The mental benefits of yoga:

- o The incorporation of breathing and meditation improves one's mental wellbeing o The regular practice of yoga can create calmness and mental clarity

o Increases body awareness

o Relieves chronic stress patterns

o Centers attention, sharpens concentration and relaxes the mind

(American Osteopathic Association, 2019)

Yoga brings attention to a number of ways we hold stress, such as clenching the jaw, which can lead to symptoms of temporomandibular joint (TMJ), grinding our teeth, tensing of the neck, shrugging our shoulders, and the stiffening of our lower back and stomach. Much of this stress also manifests in our inability to sleep properly due to high stress, an imbalance of hormones or pain, increased anxiety, and, at times, not being able to cope with the slightest of problems that would normally not be "made into mountains". (Levy, 2017)

The improvement of range of motion and flexibility can be achieved with practicing yoga regularly. Some of the yoga positions that benefit our body's flexibility are downward-facing dog, twist, forward folds, and any postures where the knees are brought to the chest.

The ability to retain balance and avoid falling is extremely important, especially for older people. It helps them continue to maintain their independence and health. (Levy, 2017)

If we feel fatigued during the day, this could be the result of poor sleep. "Brain fog" is what occurs during the afternoon and is really a normal sign that our internal clock, known as the circadian rhythm, is running well and smoothly.

Yoga is thought to be an effective way to improve and increase focus, clarity, and energy.

Stretching – even if it is only for one-two minutes, provides a massive effect on energy levels. This is especially true of people who spend hours sitting at a desk and looking at their computer screens. (Levy, 2017)

You can feel more alert and awake by bending over and touching your toes (also known as forwarding fold), back-bending in any form, squatting then standing with hands above the head, or practicing meditation or breathing exercises for a short break of five-ten minutes.

People who have back pain, especially lower back pain, will benefit from certain yoga poses that can aid in decreasing the pain. Others that can benefit are those that suffer from migraine headaches and neck pain. Yoga has made the quality of life better for people who have difficulty walking or sitting for a long period due to arthritis.

Improved blood flow and flexibility are just one aspect of the benefit of yoga. The other is the mental factors of yoga, which can also improve the tolerance of pain. People who practice yoga regularly have levels of gray matter that are healthier in their brains, especially in areas involving pain. Yoga can change your brain regarding how it handles pain and makes practicing it a natural painkiller. (Levy, 2017)

Yoga for Weight Loss / What it can do – Losing weight is simply the equation of calories in vs. calories out, changing your habits successfully, and making choices that are healthier for you. Yoga can help by putting you in tune with your body, giving you a sense of wellbeing and the improvement of your self-image. Yoga reduces stress, and in doing so, there is a reduction in the "stress eating" that may have been an obstruction in your ability to lose weight.

Ayurveda is about caring for the mind, body and spirit, and yoga ties into this practice. It encourages a healthy lifestyle that is consistent with practicing yoga, and that mindset is more likely not just to lose weight but maintain the weight loss. Most importantly, it is the ability to listen to your body, and this can be a tremendous change for those who have grappled with losing the pounds in the past. A holistic approach to weight loss is an important role that yoga plays. (Pizer, 2019)

Yoga for Weight Loss / What it can't do – Whatever yoga you practice will help to build strength. If you want to lose weight, practice yoga combined with eating as guided by your dosha and body type—or at least healthy eating and burning calories by performing exercises to upsurge the heart rate regularly along with your yoga practice. If you practice gentle yoga, then this is a must. More energetic styles of yoga can offer a livelier workout, but combine a routine of walking, running, or any other aerobic exercise that you enjoy. (Pizer, 2019)

One of the many physical benefits of yoga is how your body and muscles are stretched and become more sinuous. This is crucial because as we age and get "stiff" our joints are less flexible because the cartilage becomes thinner and the lubricating fluid decreases. Yoga can counteract this problem as many of the changes that our joints encounter is because of the lack of exercise.

As it has been stated in this chapter, numerous advantages and benefits are derived from the practice of yoga. The National Health Interview Survey (NHIS) has reported that some of the reasons that people have turned to yoga include improving overall functioning, easing lower back pain that is chronic, as a stress reducer, and the improvement of their flexibility and strength and physical fitness. It certainly counteracts the effects that sitting too much has on the body.

There are many types of yoga, some soothing and calm, while others are more intense and athletic. Here are the types of yoga and how they are practiced.

Types of Yoga

Beginners of yoga should start with a beginner level class. As you begin to practice yoga regularly, you will benefit from an instructor's attention to you as a beginner, giving instructions as to how to place your body in certain poses, as well as being able to discuss any prior injuries or medical conditions that you have to avoid any injury.

Read about the types of yoga available so that you can find a class appropriate for you.

Vinyasa is an athletic class where you will burn calories. These yoga styles commonly begin by performing a series of poses that are fast-paced and called 'sun greeting' or 'salutation'. Following the initial poses, there are a number of standing poses that keeps the yoga session moving. Once the body is warmed up, backbends and deeper stretching are performed. Vinyasa has many yoga styles. (Pizer, 2019)

Ashtanga yoga practitioners are dedicated to this vigorous style that follows the same poses each time. When all the poses are learned, the sequence enables you to practice any time—at home or in a group with an instructor, but every practitioner practices at their own pace.

Power yoga is practiced at dedicated yoga studios and popular at health clubs and gyms. This type of yoga builds on the Ashtanga strength but does not use the fixed poses series.

Hot yoga is Vinyasa yoga practiced in a room that is heated. You will sweat—*a lot.* Don't confuse Bikram and hot yoga, though, because they are not the same.

Bikram is the style that includes poses that are a fixed series. It is a pioneering style of hot yoga.

Gentle yoga, although you burn fewer calories, is still a good way to care and nurture your body. (Pizer, 2019)

Hatha yoga classes are not always gentle and have been named and used to let yoga practitioners know that these classes are *not* vinyasa classes.

Integral yoga is about integrating the mind and body. The goal is to live a happier life. People who feel distanced from their body benefit a great deal from practicing this type of yoga.

Kripalu yoga is known for its individualized approach and open acceptance of all levels of this yoga practice and body types. This is the primary choice for people who are uneasy about participating in group classes. (Pizer, 2019)

Relaxing yoga is a more passive practice of yoga. The majority of it is done in lying and seated positions. The poses are held longer and aid in you sitting for longer during meditation. Key connective tissue is stretched in this practice. It is considered a restorative and gentle yoga, usually incorporating props. There are about five to six poses that are held for more than five minutes per class. (Levy, 2017)

Practicing Yoga at Home

If you cannot get to a yoga class, you can practice at home. There are a number of online yoga websites that offer video instruction, as well as YouTube, cable TV networks like Comcast or Direct TV, and Amazon Prime.

The yoga videos can help you to increase the yoga benefits and allow you to practice a little each day. You can also begin practicing meditation at home as well. The benefits of yoga are both for the mind and body, making it an essential part of a weight loss regimen. (Pizer, 2019)

Yoga is a mind-body practice that brings together the elements of meditation, breathing control, and specific asanas (bodily poses) and is practiced all over the world.

Yoga is a stress and pain reliever, reduces the feelings of anxiety and stress, and improves the inner as well as outer balance and flexibility.

There are many types of yoga, as well as ways that we can participate if we cannot make it to a class.

We should take care to be safe when practicing yoga. Avoid some poses that may aggravate any physical or other health issues, such as asthma, sciatica, high blood pressure, to name a few conditions. If you feel you have a problem with certain poses, speak with your yoga instructor to modify or avoid it altogether. (Levy, 2017)

The best way to locate a suitable yoga class is to ask someone you trust, such as your health provider or chiropractor.

If you are new to yoga, make sure to look for an accredited instructor that is certified. Some organizations require yoga instructors to meet certain standards, such as at least 200 hours of yoga training, including a specific number of hours allocated to physiology, philosophy, anatomy, teaching methodology, and techniques. (Levy, 2017)

Enjoy the experience of yoga and incorporate it into your life. Let it become one of the many facets that are the practice of Ayurveda.

Chapter 7: Aromatherapy and Ayurveda

Aromatherapy – Ancient Tradition

Aromatherapy is based upon the Ayurvedic principles found in the scriptures of the Ancient Far East. It is the study of aromas, and the application of that knowledge is aromatherapy.

In the very beginning, before it had a name, different kinds of woods were burned, and the smoke was used in the form of incense. This practice has endured in almost all cultures in the world. (Rechelbacher, Horst, 1989)

The Egyptians first used aromatics for cosmetic purposes and medicinal techniques over 5,000 years ago. The Greeks used olive oil for the absorption of the odor from herbs and flower petals. The process was perfected by Arab physicians who distilled the oils and brought them to Europe.

Women made remedies for home use by the sixteenth century. However, pharmacology and chemistry, the new sciences of the day, reduced the practice of aromatic use to superstition, deterring the use of aromatherapy. It was not until the beginning of the twentieth century when French chemists began to research essential oils and their healing properties.

French chemist Rene Maurice Gattefosse, using oils in dermatology, discovered how lavender oil was able to heal his burned hand. Gattefosse coined the word "aromatherapy" in 1928 and used the same word as the title of a book published in 1937.

The tradition of aromatherapy remained unbroken in the Eastern cults of China and India. Indian royalty was treated with fresh and dried herbs, aromatherapy oil massage, and floral waters by ayurvedic physicians called Vaidyas. (Ayurveda, Maharishi, 2017)

Essential oils are the concentrated essences of aromatic plants and are highly concentrated. They can be derived from all parts of the plant:

- o Woods   Sandalwood
- o Leaves   Basil
- o Flowers   Rose
- o Barks   Cinnamon
- o Fruits   Orange
- o Roots   Licorice

A high degree of experience and proficiency is needed to extract the oils as it is expensive and time-consuming to achieve.

The labor-intensive process and the quantity of the plant that is needed to produce an oil make some essential oils costly. As an example, to produce jasmine oil, it takes four million jasmine flowers to yield a kilogram of the oil. However, the oils are exceptionally effective, and it takes only a few drops to achieve the effect desired.

Essential oils can be used in combination or alone. The mixing of the aroma into a cohesive increases their strength and balance the effect of individual oils.

Herbs and flowers are especially potent and pure sources when a plant is at the height of its growth, the prana or chi (life force) in a plant. The complete essence gives plants and flowers their individual essences, and the different aromas have different effects, both physiologically and psychologically on us. These essences, in their purest state, function as natural remedies and re-establish physical and mental balance. (Intelligent Nutrients, 2018)

Therapeutic Uses of Essential Oils

Smell – The pathway for aromas is the most important way through the sense of smell. Smelling the vapor of aromatic essential oils stimulates our olfactory nerve, the only nerve in our body that has direct contact with the environment and travels up to the brain. All our senses involve synaptic connections and several nerves before the impulses make contact with the brain. It is the limbic system, motivated by the olfactory nerve, that is stimulated and connected to the parts of the brain that process desires, appetites, emotions, and memories, as well as the endocrine glands that regulate the body's hormone levels. Aromas have a very powerful but subtle effect on our body and mind. (Ayurveda, Maharishi, 2017)

> o Orange blossom, chamomile, lavender, vanilla, and rose have a calming effect.
>
> o Sandalwood, nutmeg, and lavender oils help to decrease stress and its negative effects.
>
> o Patchouli oil lifts the mood, increases happiness, and reduces worry.

Massage – A widely used ayurvedic technique is aromatherapy massage. When you have one or give yourself a massage, your skin absorbs the essential oils as well as inhaling it. The essential oil penetrates the tissues and flows into the bloodstream, then moves on to the organs and systems of the body. There are different degrees of absorption. Refrain showering after a massage to ensure effectiveness.

Baths – Another popular form of aromatherapy. The warm water evaporates the essential oils sending their elements to the brain. The bath relaxes the muscles and your entire physiology, encompassed by the effects of the essence and aromas. To enjoy the full strength of the essential oils, add bath salts to the tub before you enter.

The amount of information about essential oils and their benefits is immense. Some of the oils fight inflammation, infection, and other ailments. They are effective and help do away with some illnesses and conditions that medical prescriptions are not as effective against, including creating unwanted side effects.

Benefits of Using Essential Oils for Common Ailments

There is a myriad of uses for essential oils. Some of the ailments we suffer from are common, everyday maladies, and others are more complex. Here are three essential oils that can relieve some illnesses:

Turmeric oil – Known for its antioxidant, anti-inflammatory, anti-malarial, anti-tumor, anti-microbial, and anti-aging properties. Turmeric is a spice, a medicine, and a coloring agent. The essential oil is an extraordinary health agent and one that seems to have the most promising effects against cancer.

Turmeric oil is thought to be a strong balancer and relaxer of the body. Its benefits also come from the healthful vitamins, phenols, and other alkaloids. All these beneficial components show that turmeric essential oil holds these health benefits:

  o **Helps combat breast cancer** – can hinder TPA abilities, a potent promoter of tumors
  o **Leukemia cells** – can destroy some by aromatic turmerone
  o **Arthritis** – aids in reducing joint issues, arthritis and its inflammation
  o **Liver** – improves health
  o **Neurologic disease**
  o **Depression and anxiety**

Oregano oil – Antibiotics are designed for fighting off bacterial infections and are one of a medical doctor's go-to way for treating many health conditions. However, there is an underutilized natural oil from oregano that patients don't know about, and thus, doctors tell their patients. (Axe, Dr. Josh, 2018)

You may think about the oregano leaves that you use to cook with or as a topping you put on your pizza, but essential oregano oil is far from being a food simplicity. It takes 1,000 pounds of wild oregano for the production of one pound of oregano essential oil. The active ingredients of the oil are preserved in alcohol and used in either essential oil form, both internally and topically.

A powerful plant-derived essential oil, oregano may be a competitor against antibiotics when it comes to the prevention or treatment of various infections. Oregano oil has properties that are antiviral, antibacterial, and antifungal. And the most positive thing about using oregano oil is that it is not likely to cause any side effects that can be harmful and that are most commonly linked to the high use of antibiotics, such as the risk of resistance to antibiotics, reduced vitamin absorption (due to damage of the GI tract's lining that creates a leaky gut syndrome), and the destruction of beneficial probiotic bacteria. (Axe, Dr. Josh, 2018)

Oregano oil benefits almost make it a "wonder oil" because it goes beyond controlling infections. Other examples of the types of conditions oregano can help are:

> o **Common colds** – as a natural antibiotic, take internally mixed in water or coconut oil
> o **Gingivitis** – combine oregano oil with coconut oil and use for oil pulling
> o **Athlete's foot or toenail fungus** – put directly on the area twice a day

Evening Primrose Oil – Impacts the health of your hormones, hair, bones, and skin.

Evening primrose oil is located as a wildflower found growing in Central and Eastern North America. Native Americans and settlers from Europe used evening primrose for food. In order to extract the oil, the flower's seeds are cold pressed. Essential fatty acids in elevated levels are found in evening primrose and are necessary for our health. However, the body cannot produce fatty acids—you have to get them through food. Omega-6 fatty acids are critical for brain function along with omega-3 fatty acids. Our bodies need the omega-6 as well as omega-3, found in fish oils. Fats aid the slowing of our ability to absorb nutrients. This process helps to control our hunger for longer periods. Fatty acid additionally acts to transport vitamins like vitamin E, vitamin A, and vitamin K.

Evening primrose oil reduces the pain connected to PMS, is an anti-inflammatory that is helpful for the symptoms of menopause and rheumatoid arthritis and osteoporosis, and improves skin conditions, such as acne, psoriasis, and eczema. (Axe, DC, DMN, CNS, Dr. Josh, 2018)

Aromatherapy for Balance

Ayurveda is about the restoration of balance to the mind, body, and spirit. Vata, Pitta, and Kapha control all the workings of the mind and body and have seasons associated with them. Vata associates with fall and winter. Kapha associates with spring, and Pitta associates with summer. There are aroma blends that are traditional and useful for the overall restoring of personal balance.

Vata's balancing blends include warming oils that are sweet and soothe the emotions and the mind and enhance serenity. Sweet Orange, Ylang Ylan, Geranium Rose and Frankincense are examples.

Try equal parts of Ylang and Frankincense, about two-four drops each, and mix in two oz. of a light massage oil like Sweet Almond or Jojoba for a therapeutic, relaxing full-body massage. Combining two drops of Sweet Orange, two drops of Lemon and four drops of

Jasmine can help you to unwind. This is a blend to be tried in a late evening bath.

Pitta tends to become imbalanced in situations of extreme heat, whether it is emotion-related or weather-related. The aroma blends for Pitta to become balanced include cooling sweet oils, such as Ylang Ylang and Frankincense, and some uplifting oils, such as Peppermint or Lemon. The combinations are meant to keep you calm yet alert and focused. Another combination is four drops each of Sandalwood and Ylang Ylang for an infusion for your bathwater on hot days.

To create a calm environment and diffusing intensity, blend equal parts of Vetiver, Sandalwood, Rose, Jasmine, and Fennel and use the quantity in an aroma diffuser.

Kapha's warm, invigorating and spicy blends are meant to wake you up on a cold, gray, damp spring day. Vital oils are Peppermint, Rosemary, Eucalyptus, and Basie, with smaller amounts of oils such as Ylang Ylang or Frankincense for balancing.

Try four drops of Peppermint and two drops each of Ylang Ylang and Frankincense as a morning bath infusion or as part of your shower gel by using four-six drops per two oz. of unscented cleanser and feel the invigorating aromas balance your mind and body long after you have bathed.

Healing scents afford the gentle balance for the body, mind, and spirit. Please note that oils are potent substances; less is more with many of the oils. Take care in both using and blending the oils. Always dilute oils before bringing them in contact with your skin and always test for skin sensitivity. Consult with your physician if you are pregnant before using any essential oils. Remember, these oils are for external use only.

Aromatherapy has many applications; even if your schedule is busy, you can spend time enjoying its benefits. Light up an aromatic candle while you cook or bathe, or place a car diffuser in your car on your way to work or when running errands.

Essential oils have a very powerful effect yet take up little space. Use them as often as you wish.

Chapter 8: Ayurvedic Meditation

Ayurveda and Meditation

Meditation is the practice of training one's mind to bring about consciousness and is a type of mind & body exercise. It is a number of techniques that promote relaxation, help in building internal energy and evoke compassion. It also helps to achieve mental and physical calm and increases health and treatment of diseases. (AyurvedDoctor, 2019)

Meditation has become a popular way to relieve stress for millions of people around the world. It can take on many forms and can be used in numerous important ways. It can help you reverse the stress in your mind and body and can also be used when you are imbalanced to become centered. Meditation, as already touched on, can even boost healthier eating and weight loss.

Meditation is the art of achieving the discipline of the mind to get away from the "impulsive busyness" and get into a calm and relaxed state. Several meditative principles accentuate on various spiritual and physical practices with numerous goals like the achievement of self-awareness, creativity, higher consciousness, or a peaceful mind.

Ayurveda and your mind - Ayurveda treats the mind as a microscopic element that consists of three qualities known as Trigunas: Tamas, Rajas, and Sattva. This concept is comparable to the Vata Dosha as it is swift and unstable. It traverses from past to future in a nanosecond. The chaos in the mind can create unrest in a person and a collected, composed, and calm mind is the flourishing of ground for creative work and a healthy body. (AyurvedDoctor, 2019)

What environment is needed for meditation? - To begin meditation, it is always good to have a quiet and calm location. A comfortable posture is also important as it lets you focus on one thing at a time. Focus your thought on one object or thing at a time. Concentrate on this and keep from letting your thoughts wander. (AyurvedDoctor, 2019)

What time is considered ideal for meditation? - Meditating before sunrise is the ideal time, known in Ayurveda as Brahma Muhurta. This is the time when nature is completely quiet, with no noise or disturbance. (AyurvedDoctor, 2019)

Instructions for Ayurvedic Meditation

o Have a time of silence that is undisturbed in a peaceful, calm environment.

o To begin meditation, sit in a position that is comfortable, on a cushion or rug on the floor. If this is not possible, sit in a comfortable chair, making sure your feet touch the floor.

o Let your body be as still as possible, sitting erect to allow for the energy in your body to flow without obstruction, all through your head and descending the spine. This creates balance in the body.

o Close your eyes and allow them to relax. Think of any object. Focus your concentration on the object while you inhale and then exhale.

o Allow your mind to wander because, at first, you will experience thoughts coming into your mind from all directions.

o Concentrate on your breathing, noticing its gentle sound. As you continue concentrating and breathing, the other random thoughts will begin to disperse, and your mind will become quieter. Slowly the thoughts will start decreasing, and your mind will become quieter.

o Stresses are released, and the more powerful the release of the stress, the more powerful and absorbing the thoughts and it will reach a point when there will only be quiet and calm enveloping the mind.

o Try to incorporate meditation two times a day if possible. In the beginning, meditate and build up to that length of time. Once you can master the amount of time, you can meditate more often or for longer periods. However, meditating for short periods each day is better than meditating in lengthy times irregularly. Meditation and its benefits are greater than any supposed problems that may be perceived. (Murray, 2013)

Focusing on a sound will help you to work towards a deep meditation. A meditation that promotes this is the So Hum meditation.

Types of meditation

Concentrative meditation – This type of meditation facilitates the use of one's breathing, a sound or picture to help quiet the mind. Yoga and Ayurveda believe in a strong connection between one's mind and breathing. Regular slow, deep breaths bring a calmness to the mind. When your mind is focused on breathing it easily gets immersed in the rhythm of your breathing pattern. (AyurvedDoctor, 2019)

Mindful meditation – These meditations allow you to recognize the contents around you like the smells, sounds, thoughts, and the like while not identifying with the content. It is one of the most important Buddhist meditations. The person practicing this sits quietly and allows the mind to wander without reacting to the content that surrounds them. Thoughts are in the present moment in mindful meditation.

Transcendental Meditation (TM) – This meditation has origins with Lord Krishna. References in the Buddhist works allude to this type of meditation. From Shankaracharya to Brahmannada Saraswati passed on the knowledge of Transcendental Meditation. However, the Maharshi Mahesh Yogi made this meditation famous worldwide. He explains how natural the technique is and stated, "The practice of TM is to think of a word that is devoid of meaning." (AyurvedDoctor, 2019)

TM is a silent state of mind based on sound meditation. Each person is provided with a mantra according to his/her thought. (TM Admin, 2015)

Some mantras have certain meanings; however, you can develop your own mantra that is solely for you to use and resonates what you feel while you meditate. The mantra can be about where you want to get to, i.e., "I am calm" is a mantra you can repeat to help you feel calm and relieve any anxiety you may have. Another mantra is *aum (pronounced ah-um)*. It is a sacred sound and generally known as the "sound of the Universe". This is the most famous mantra. Many people also use it for what their reason is at the time of meditation.

So Hum meditation – This meditation uses the natural sound of your breathing—meaning the sound that is produced during the breathing process. When a person begins to concentrate on the sound of his/her breathing, the mind starts to become immersed in the sound and slowly becomes more and more focused.

Vipassana Meditation – Buddha taught this meditation. The definition of Vipassana means to see things clearly. The focus and purpose of this meditation are to remove impurities and toxins from the body. This meditation is intense because it asks the person to search for their inner soul and maintain complete silence for a week.

Loving-Kindness Meditation – This is one of the most popular meditations. Those who enjoy practicing this meditation can increase their ability to forgive, self-accept, connect with others, and much more. This meditation also has powerful aspects for the relief of stress. Loving-kindness meditation is easy to practice and can increase the feeling of happiness in minutes. (Scott, 2018)

The main point of loving-kindness meditation is to concentrate on loving and caring energy towards others and oneself. It is clear what the benefits are—those who practice experience all the usual benefits from meditating, which are several and vast, as well as feelings of love, kindness, and warmth.

As with any meditation, allow time to meditate. Be seated comfortably, close your eyes, relax the muscles of your body, and begin by taking some deep breaths. The experience of competing for emotional and physical wellness and inner peace is what you will imagine as you begin. Focus on the feeling of inner peace as you are exhaling out tension and inhaling feelings of love.

Repeat three or four positive and reassuring phrases to yourself. Many can work, but these are some examples:

o May I be happy

o May I be strong, healthy, and peaceful

o May I give and receive appreciation today and every day

You may remain with this focus during your meditation, or move your focus to loved ones—a spouse, parent, or child, then repeat the following phrases or ones that are similar to bring about feelings of love and kindness:

- o May you be happy
- o May you be strong, healthy, and peaceful
- o May you be safe
- o May you give and receive appreciation today

This mediation continues to bring other people who are important to us into our awareness and inner peace. Once you have held these feelings towards each person, bring other important people from your life into your awareness, one by one, and visualize them with wellness and inner peace.

When you complete the meditation, remember that you can revisit the feeling of loving kindness throughout the day.

Zen meditation – This is a meditation technique entrenched in Buddhist psychology. The goal of the meditation is to control attention. It is sometimes referred to as a practice that involves "thinking about not thinking." (Morin, 2019)

Zen meditation is thought to be an "open-monitoring meditation". The skills that monitor are altered into a state of awareness with an extensive scope of attention, without concentrating on one specific object.

Zen allows you to open your mind and relax your body to discover your inner self. Once you master this type of mediation after days of practice, you can reach a meditative state where your breathing will become shallow, and your heartbeat will slow down. Thoughts will be isolated, and you can concentrate consciously on the present moment. (AyurvedDoctor, 2019)

Similar to mindfulness meditation, its focus is the presence of mind. However, mindfulness focuses on a specific object, while Zen meditation is about general awareness.

Zen is unlike loving-kindness meditation, which focuses on nurturing compassion, or the mantra meditation, such as Transcendental Meditation that involves the reciting of a mantra; Zen involves the ongoing self-referential and physical processes. Those who practice Zen try to expand their range of attention to integrate the flow of thoughts, emotional perceptions, and subjective consciousness. (Morin, 2019)

The Benefits of Meditation

One of the major issues we experience throughout the day is stress. Our bodies react in ways that have us prepared to "fight or flight". Our minds are stressed from the avalanche of thoughts and intake of information we experience every single day. Your family issues, job issues, other people issues, and the world around us all play a part in the psychological stress that we experience.

Meditation is the exact opposite of the stress we feel and affects our body and mind by sparking the body's response to relaxation. It reinstates the body to a state of calm, helping it repair itself and averting any new damage from the physical effects of stress. Meditation can bring calm to the mind and body by silencing the thoughts that we have that are stress-induced, and that can keep our body's response to stress continually triggered.

With regular practice, there is a greater gain that meditation can bring, and that is long-term resilience. It has been shown via research that those who meditate regularly begin to feel changes in response to stress. That allows them to recover easier from situations that are stressful and experience the feelings of stress much less against the challenges they may have to endure in their everyday lives. There is an increase in positive moods that can come when we meditate; research has shown that experiencing moods that are positive more often are more buoyant toward stress. It has also been found that regular meditation changes the brain in its decreased reactivity toward stress. (Scott M. E., 2019)

Meditation Provides More Benefits

The benefits of meditation can, among other things, reverse your response to stress and protect you from developing chronic stress.

When you practice meditation your blood pressure becomes normal, your use of oxygen is more economical, your breathing and heart rate slow down, the function of your immune system improves, and the adrenal glands produce less cortisol, which is important if you are trying to lose weight. You also perspire less, your creativity increases, and your mind becomes clearer and ages at a slower rate.

Habits that can damage the body, such as drinking, smoking, and drugs, can be eliminated easier by people who meditate regularly. This is not to say it happens overnight, but many people find that they can connect to their inner strength. Meditation can build resilience and minimize stress.

How Does Meditation Compare to Other Stress Reduction Methods?

Meditation has been compared to other stress-reducing methods. However, unlike some prescribed medications and herbal therapies, there are few side effects from meditating.

The physical limitations that many people have because of age or infirmity allows them to practice meditation rather than practice strenuous exercise to relieve their stress.

There is no special equipment that is necessary to practice meditation, except for a comfortable pillow for the floor or chair.

There is absolutely no monetary expenditure involved— meditation is free

Meditating regularly requires commitment and discipline. It may be more difficult to maintain as a habit. A meditation group that meets regularly may be the answer.

Freeing the mind from the thoughts of the day is particularly difficult for some people. This may be even more difficult than maintaining meditation as a regular habit. Focus on your thoughts by journaling or other methods that distract the mind, such as using humor or doing physical therapy.

By learning meditation to calm your mind and body, your emotional and physical stress can be managed, and emotional stress can be dissolved. Meditation leaves you feeling refreshed, feeling better, and ready to meet the day's challenges. Most importantly, you feel peace within yourself. It gives you a healthy attitude, and with regular practice, you will experience these benefits even more.

Chapter 9: Ayurveda Natural Beauty Tips

Women and men always want to look and feel their best. Yet there has been a growing trend of artificial "fixes" such as synthetic serums that are injected into the body that is supposed to help with our appearance. Sometimes there are side effects to introducing synthetic substances into our bodies.

Ayurveda is an early adopter of the adage, "beauty comes from within." Balancing the body, mind, and spirit, optimizing energy, supporting the health of our digestive system, and observing the individual needs of our dosha is how this inner beauty happens. What happens when the inner beauty is administered to and cared for is that the outer beauty reflects it and shines through.

However, it isn't that you should ignore your outer beauty, like your hair and skin. Ayurveda provides many beauty practices, and they will all make you glow while boosting your wellbeing.

In Ayurveda, there are more oils used than lotions or creams. Part of detoxing includes exfoliation. Some of the top Ayurvedic practitioners share their beauty tips, all-natural and holistic, that that you can do easily and are cost-efficient as well. Incorporate them into your beauty regimen for that inner-outer balance of beauty. (Abel, 2017)

Your dosha dictates your skin needs – Your dosha, or what is known as your Ayurvedic constitution, points to your skin type:

> o **Vata** is thin, fine-pored, dry, delicate, and prone to wrinkle;
>
> o **Pitta** has breakouts, rashes, and rosacea if imbalanced; and
>
> o **Kapha** is thick, oily, has enlarged pores, pimples, blackheads, and eczema.

Your skin may not reflect what has been described for each dosha, but remember that we are a combination of all three doshas. Follow the description that best matches how your skin behaves.

Coconut Oil – Use coconut oil to moisturize your face and make facial masks as it is light and cooling. Some women also use ghee (clarified butter). Masks are really refreshing for your skin. If your skin is dry and irritated, it will rejuvenate with an organic castor oil mask. If you have oily skin, use chickpea flour as a base for masks to absorb excess oil from your face, back, and chest. (Abel, 2017)

Raw Milk – Masks made from cream-based or full-fat milk are cooling and soothing if you have inflamed skin. To remove dirt from your pores, dip a cotton ball into raw milk. When you bathe, adding cream or milk to your bath will nourish and soothe your skin. If you are a vegan, coconut milk has very similar properties.

Sugar – Sugar helps to retain moisture and promote cell turnover. It is considered cooling—mix sugar with rejuvenating botanicals and herbs like slippery elm and rose petals.

Rosewater – Rosewater spray feels great and has a beautiful fragrance. You can use it several times a day, and it supports supple skin and is cooling.

Neem oil – When you have pimples or minor spots of inflammation, apply neem oil and wake up to the magic that happens overnight. Neem oil is similar to tea tree oil as it dries inflammations but is more cooling. (Abel, 2017)

Aloe vera - Aloe vera can make your skin supple, smooth, and younger-looking. Some women drink a small amount alone or drink it in a juice, while others use it topically as a toner or treatment.

Coconut oil and your hair - While you give your hair a luster and sheen by brushing your hair with coconut oil, it also provides nourishment and strengthening. Add some essential oils like rosemary, lavender, and geranium and take time massaging it into your hair and scalp. It takes away dead skin cells, improves circulation, and helps your hair grow.

Oil Pulling - Instead of using alcohol-based mouthwash like Listerine, swishing coconut or sesame oil has become quite a popular practice. It also benefits your mouth and gums, and aids in total detoxification.

Self-Massage - Let the warm oil be poured and get a massage. It deeply moisturizes and provides many health benefits when it is done regularly. It also helps manage stress, and afterward, you look radiant. If you can't get away to a spa, use an Ayurvedic oil of your choice like chamomile and work from your face down to the soles of your feet. Even a few minutes before bedtime will help you soothe your body, and you will have a beautiful fragrance to fall asleep with.

Oil your body before showering, on an empty stomach, in the morning, and your head, feet an ears before you sleep at night.

Don't oil your body if you are having trouble with your bowels—either with constipation or diarrhea—are menstruating, have a cold or cough, or have a fever because of illness. Also, avoid oiling areas that have rashes or wounds if it is cloudy or rainy because it will be difficult for your body to absorb oil.

Brush your body - For firm and toned skin, help with cellulite, and places that store excess water, dry brush your body. For Vata and Pitta skin types, use a raw silk gharshana glove for a less abrasive exfoliation. Use a natural bristle brush for the Kapha skin type. (Abel, 2017)

Be Active - Exercise can improve your skin health. When your body perspires, and your blood circulates, it helps the body rid itself of toxins and can leave you with glowing, healthy skin. (Mulumba, 2019)

Seeds and Nuts - Seeds and nuts are rich in omega-3, healthy fats, and vitamin E. Eat nuts, flax seeds, sunflower seeds, pumpkin, and chia seeds to boost your skin health.

Drink tea – Keeping hydrated throughout the day is important. Sip on herbal tea as well as water. Chamomile, ginger, or lemon tea can help keep your digestive tract healthy. A healthy digestive system keeps the skin glowing. (Sinha, 2019)

Breathe – Today's world can emit much stress for anyone, but if you suffer from chronic stress, it can affect your balance and wellbeing. Acne breakouts and premature aging can be exacerbated by stress.

It is critical to find ways to de-stress and bring the levels of anxiety down a few notches. One way is through breathing exercises and meditation. Breathing can give the cells of your skin oxygen and keep the skin healthy. (Mulumba, 2019)

Stop and listen to how you are breathing. Observe where your breath is coming from. It is possible that you're breathing too shallow using the upper chest. It is recommended that you breath slow and deep so that you feel the air come into your abdomen. If you want help in deep breathing, use jasmine, rose, or lavender as your essential oil to inhale. Deep breathing brings serenity and calmness—the essential elements of beauty. (Ayurerveda, Maharishi, 2019)

Get Your Sleep - Sleep is as much a necessity for survival as food and water. Sleep is when your body rejuvenates, repairs, and replenishes skin cells, and, in fact, all the damaged cells in your body through the process of autophagy—the process where the body's cells are cleaned and renewed. If your sleep is poor, interrupted, or you are generally not getting enough of it, you will begin to see a dull, aged individual in the mirror. Sleep a minimum of seven hours a night to promote good health and appearance. (Mulumba, 2019)

Turn Down the Noise – You may not be able to buy a retreat on a remote island or up in the mountains to get more silence in your life, but you can turn down the noise by filtering out the things that are on constantly—the computer, phone, TV, and even conversations. Tune them out and tune into your inner self; true silence that enables you to connect with yourself. The philosophy of Ayurveda says this increases your spirituality, deepens it, and makes you a person of substance.

Make the time at least two to three times a week for twenty minutes to shut the door, light a candle filled with an essential oil that balances you, close your eyes, and absorb the silence and peace, the serenity and calmness. You will feel rejuvenated and appreciate it the more you practice.

Get Rid of Those Bags Under Your Eyes

As we age, bags under the eyes are a common development that, frankly, no one likes. When we look in the mirror and see those bags, the feeling of being youthful and attractive is hard to muster.

A number of natural, at-home remedies can be applied, as well as getting rid of some bad habits, that can help decrease those bags and help with allergies:

Peppermint oil – diffuse five drops of the oil at home to treat a scratchy throat and unclog the sinus. It can be added to a cup of tea, water, or a smoothie.

Basil Oil – works very well against allergens and reduces inflammation.

Reduce Salt intake – high blood pressure is linked to salt, but all sodium can promote fluid retention that can lead to undereye puffiness. Use pure Himalayan sea salt if you want to use salt, but moderately. Salty foods, such as pizza, potato chips, and some soups, can wreak havoc on fluid retention. Celery can help curb your salt desire, and fresh vegetables are a great option too.

Exercise – exercise has always been a natural way to promote a youthful glow and reduce the signs of aging, but the eye area will benefit from exercises specifically designed for the face. The book *The Yoga Facelift* by Marie-Veronique Nadeau shows how facial yoga exercises are slow facial muscle exercises that tighten and tone. The exercises involve using light pressure from your fingers to act as resistance.

Yoga is also beneficial. The various poses executed in yoga can help increase the blood circulating to the face, take away excess fluid, and give relief from swelling.

Remove your makeup – before you retire for the evening, wash any makeup off, especially eye makeup. The day-long makeup has accumulated dirt and dust from the environment. Letting your face and eye makeup remain on your face and eyes can cause irritation, puffiness, and watery eyes. Gently remove the makeup and add some soothing natural eye cream. (Oliver, 2018)

Your sleep position – it can be difficult to change the position you sleep in, but sleeping on your back can avoid fluid building up around the eyes. Add an extra pillow under your head for effective sleep. If you find sleeping on your back difficult, try to sleep on your side. Don't sleep on your stomach, or with your face in the pillows.

Alcohol: Limit or Eliminate – your skin and body dehydrate when you drink alcohol, and the delicate area around your eyes can appear dark and sunken. Alcohol also causes the eyes to be tired and bloodshot. Limit alcohol intake to once a day and drink more water. You will feel fresher, your eyes will benefit, and the skin around the eyes will be more hydrated. (Oliver, 2018)

Stop Smoking – cigarettes weaken and dry out your facial skin as well as the entire body, and your eyes prematurely age. The chemicals found in cigarettes are noxious and cause eye irritation, which could promote undereye bags or dark circles. There are many reasons to stop smoking. You may want to investigate some natural ways to quit.

Try a Neti Pot – this is a remedy that can be a part of your daily routine to reduce the puffiness around the eyes. The neti pot originated in Ayurvedic medicine in India. It looks like a small teapot and can be purchased in most health food stores. It helps to flush the sinuses of extra moisture from infections, colds, or allergies that crop up during the allergy season.

Fill the pot with water and add half a tablespoon of sea salt. Pour the saltwater into one nostril and allow it to drain out the other nostril over your bathroom sink. It is a strange feeling, at first, but it is very refreshing and will cleanse your sinuses. (Oliver, 2018)

Ayurveda offers so many beauty tips that help you to feel refreshed, calm, and healthy. Follow these natural ways to care for your body, skin, and hair, and begin to see noticeable differences in time. True beauty is the combination of three elements: a balanced mind, a nourished body, and a peaceful spirit. Attaining the three may seem difficult, but the beauty secrets are incredibly simple. Use this chapter as a guide to beautify and care for yourself each day, each season, and each year.

Chapter 10: Ayurvedic Recipes and Beverages

One of the points of the Ayurveda lifestyle is choices. A healthy diet is a significant part of obtaining and maintaining good health.

Here are some recipes for both meals and beverages that are conducive with the three doshas, Vata, Pitta, and Kapha. Options are noted in each recipe to note any changes or elimination of certain ingredients to satisfy each constitution.

Upma – Breakfast

This south Indian breakfast dish is savory and delicious. Upma is also eaten with other meals and is easy to prepare.

Roasting aids in reducing glutamine.

If the chili and mustard seeds are increased, Kapha can consume in moderation. Bear Mush is similar to Cream of Wheat—farina that is quick to cook.

This dish is a balance for all three doshas:

Ingredients

1 cup Bear Mush or creamed wheat

½ tsp turmeric

½ cup safflower oil or ghee

1tsp cumin seeds

1tsp black mustard seeds

1 pinch hing

1 small green chili, finely chopped

¼ cup cilantro leaves, chopped

1 small onion, chopped

½ tsp salt

3 cups coconut water

Cilantro for garnish

Preparation

In a pan, roast creamed wheat over medium heat until browned. Frequently shake or stir. Remove from heat. Set aside in a bowl.

Heat a saucepan over medium heat. Add ghee or oil, cumin, and mustard seeds. Add spices when seeds pop, except for salt. Add in cilantro, chili, and onion. Cook until the onion is browned. Add water and salt. Boil. Slowly stir in the roasted creamed wheat. Allow to boil for one-two minutes, continuously stirring to avoid lumps.

Add coconut and chopped cilantro leaves for garnish.

Squeeze fresh lime on each serving.

Chapatis

Makes twelve.

In place of chapati flour, use whole wheat pastry flour.

This dish is balanced for all three doshas:

Ingredients

4 cups whole wheat flour

¾ tsp salt

2 cups water

Safflower oil in a small bowl

Preparation

Mix flour and salt. Create a hole in the middle of the flour. Add water, a quarter of a cup each time, and use hands to knead the dough after each addition of water.

Continue adding water and knead until the dough is stiff and does not stick to hands. More or less water may be needed to achieve this consistency, depending on the climate and the humidity level.

Set aside and cover the dough for half an hour.

After the dough has set, make the dough approximately the size of a small egg.

Roll into a ball, then roll the ball in flour. Flatten with rolling pin or hand.

Brush or pat one side with oil, avoiding the edges.

Lightly dip into flour on the oiled side. Fold over halfway. Cover the oiled side. Fold again. Pinch edges together.

Dip in flour, then roll out to be even and thin, about five inches across in a round shape. Turn chapati each time before rolling again.

Place the chapati in a hot pan that is seasoned. Cook until chapati bubbles up and the bottom is browned. Pan should not be oily. Only oil is on chapati that is brushed on one side at a time to cook.

Dab oil, flip onto the other side. Cook until lightly brown.

Cook chapati for two-four minutes. Wrap in a towel until served.

Vegetable Spiced Rice – Marsala Rice

Serves four-five

A versatile dish that is good to serve in late spring or early summer. It is a quick-cooking recipe that is just right for the end of the day.

Ingredients

2 cups basmati rice

½ cup fresh cilantro, chopped (divided use)

½ cup green beans, chopped

½ cup zucchini, chopped

½ cup peas, fresh (can substitute broccoli, cauliflower, potatoes or carrots according to the constitution)

2 pinches salt

½ tsp mustard seeds

½ tsp cumin

¼ tsp turmeric

A pinch asafetida (hing)

3 cloves garlic, finely chopped

12-14 whole cloves

2 cinnamon sticks, small pieces

1 inch ginger, fresh, finely diced, peeled

10 whole cardamom pods

1 pinch cayenne

6-10 bay leaves

½ cup ghee

1 tbs coconut shredded

1 lime

Preparation

Wash rice twice. Wash and chop vegetables. In a blender, put chopped ginger and a quarter of a cup of cilantro with half a cup of water and shredded coconut. Blend until liquefied.

In a three-quarter saucepan, heat ghee. Add cumin seeds, hing, turmeric, and mustard seeds. Cook until mustard seeds pop. Add bay leaves, cardamom, cloves, and cinnamon. Heat until spices are fragrant. Pour in the mixture from blender. Add salt and garlic. Cook until garlic is slightly browned. Stir in rice and vegetables and mix thoroughly, then add cayenne. Pour in five cups of water to boil. Reduce heat, simmer, and cover loosely.

Cook for up to eighteen-twenty minutes (until the rice is cooked and the vegetables are tender). Place in a serving dish and squeeze over the fresh lime juice. Sprinkle shredded coconut and chopped cilantro on top before serving.

Kitchari – Ancient Food / Modern Times

This is an ancient recipe. Its composition is mung dal and basmati rice and has as many varied ways of being made as there is the number of people who cook it. Kitchari is cooked in one pot. The vegetables and spices can generate a balance for the three doshas. It is easy and quick to prepare, and is a popular dish for almost every lifestyle.

The tridoshic combination is a good protein combination of mung dal and basmati rice that create a balanced food. It is a complete food that provides vitality and strength and is easy to digest. It gives nourishment to all tissues of the body.

Kitchari usually means a mixture of two grains. There are alternatives to the recipe to satisfy the doshas. Kitchari is the food most preferred to use when going through cleansing programs or on a mono-fast. Kitchari also rejuvenates cells and detoxifies.

Options: sweet potato, zucchini, asparagus

Vata or Kapha – a pinch of ginger powder

Pitta – eliminate mustard seeds

Ingredients

½ cup basmati rice

6 cups water

1 cup mung dal, split yellow

½ tsp to an inch ginger root, grated or chopped

¼ tsp mineral salt

2 tbs ghee

½ tsp coriander powder

½ tsp cumin, whole seeds

½ tsp cumin, powder form

½ tsp turmeric, powder form

½ tsp mustard seeds

A handful of cilantro leaves

1 ½ cups assorted vegetables (optional)

Preparation

Carefully remove any stones from rice and dal. Wash each separately. Change the water twice during washing for each. Combine in a pot. Add six cups of water. Cover and cook for about twenty minutes until soft.

While rice and dal are cooking, prepare any vegetables and cut into small pieces. Add vegetables to rice and dal. Cook for an additional ten minutes. Sauté the seeds in the ghee until they pop. Put in other spices and stir rice, dal, and vegetables.

Add mineral salt, chopped cilantro, and serve.

Teas for Each Dosha

Add ingredients in equal parts for all teas:

Vata tea – coriander, cumin, and ground ginger

Pitta tea – fennel, coriander, and cumin

Kapha tea – cinnamon, ground ginger, a pinch of clove

VEGETABLES

Celery and Aubergine

Ingredients

1 large aubergine, cut into chunks

4 celery stalks, chopped

1 cup coriander

Pinch of turmeric

½ tsp ghee

Salt & pepper (optional)

Preparation

Place half a teaspoon of ghee in a wok. Heat. Add turmeric and celery.

Fry for two minutes, stirring constantly. Add half a cup of hot water. Cook on medium heat until liquid evaporates.

Add aubergine and half of the coriander. Fry for another minute.

Add half a liter of hot water and boil. Then lower the heat. Cook until vegetables soften. Add the remaining coriander and salt and pepper. Serve.

Aubergine and Courgettes

Ingredients

3 medium courgettes

1 large aubergine

½ tsp turmeric

1 tsp grated beetroot

1 tsp salt

1 tsp thyme

1 tsp basil

1 bay leaf

1 tbs ghee

Preparation

Chop courgettes and aubergine into thick pieces.

Stir fry the courgettes and aubergine for one to two minutes in the ghee.

Add two cups of hot water and all other ingredients. Simmer for five minutes.

Add beetroot and turmeric. Serve.

Tasty Broth

Ingredients

1 large celery stick

5 carrots, juiced

3 cauliflower leaves

3 large slices ginger root

½ pineapple, diced

1 tsp fennel seeds

1 cup coriander, fresh, chopped

1tsp salt

1 tsp pepper

Preparation

Heat one and a half liters of water in a saucepan. Add all of the ingredients, except for the coriander and carrot juice, and simmer until cooked. Strain.

Add coriander and carrot juice. Serve.

Vegetable Stew

Ingredients

5 medium carrots, chopped into sticks

1 medium butternut squash, chopped

1 medium aubergine, diced

2 courgettes, diced

I fennel bulb, chopped

½ tsp paprika

½ tsp thyme

Salt & pepper

Preparation

Fry the herbs and spices in the ghee. Add carrots, fennel, and 1 cup of hot water.

When the liquid has evaporated, add the other vegetables and 1 liter of hot water. Cook for 30 minutes.

Add salt and pepper to taste. Serve.

Spicy Courgettes

Ingredients

2 medium courgettes, cut into thin strips

2 tsp grated ginger

1 tsp ghee

½ cup carrot juice

Preparation

Prepare the courgettes. Heat the ghee. Fry ginger until golden brown.

Add courgettes. Continue to fry until slightly browned. Stir occasionally.

Add the carrot juice and simmer until the courgettes are tender and the liquid is almost evaporated. Serve.

Spinach & Celery

Ingredients

1 tbs ghee

3½ lbs spinach

6 celery stalks, cut into small pieces

½ tsp nutmeg, grated

1 tsp vata churna

1 tbs soy sauce

1 tbs thyme

1 tbs tarragon

Preparation

Heat the ghee and sauté the spinach. Cover with water so that the spinach is only just submerged.

Add all ingredients, except for the nutmeg. Simmer for approximately ten minutes.

Serve warm and sprinkle with nutmeg.

Chunky Veg

Ingredients

1 aubergine

4 baby mooli

2 courgettes

1 tsp kapha churna or jerk

1-2 tsp ghee

Preparation

Chop vegetables into large chunky pieces. Mix mooli and courgettes with spices, then let sit for fifteen minutes.

Heat half the ghee in a wok and stir-fry the aubergine for one min. Remove and set aside.

Add the remaining ghee, mooli, and courgettes to the wok. Stir fry for two minutes.

Add 1 cup of boiling water. Simmer until water evaporates. Add the aubergine and 2 more cups of boiling water. Simmer until vegetables are cooked.

Serve.

Glazed Carrots

Ingredients

8 oz carrots, sliced

½ tsp ghee

1 tbs soy sauce

1 tsp maple syrup

Preparation

Steam or boil the carrots until they are tender. Strain.

Heat the ghee in a pan. Stir-fry carrots until slightly browned.

Add soy sauce and maple syrup.

Toss and serve.

Curried Sweet Potatoes

Ingredients

2 sweet potatoes, cubed

½ leek stem, sliced

1 garlic clove, chopped (or a pinch of hing)

1 tsp kapha churna ghee

½ tsp turmeric

½ tsp black pepper,

½ tsp salt

Preparation

Preheat oven to 375°.

Boil sweet potatoes until almost cooked. Strain (keep the liquid to the side).

Heat a wok with ghee. Add the leek and garlic. Fry until golden brown.

Add the spices and stir for one minute. Add potatoes and stir for two minutes.

Add the water from the boiled potatoes. Bring to the boil, then lower the heat. Cook until the liquid is reduced by half.

Place into a baking dish and cook for half an hour. Serve.

Fennel & Red Peppers

Ingredients

2 fennel bulbs, large chunks (steamed)

1 red pepper, cut into strips

Sesame seeds (optional)

1tsp ghee

1 cup hot water

Preparation

Heat wok with the ghee. Add the sesame seeds and fry for one minute.

Add the fennel and red pepper. Fry for one to two minutes. Add one cup of hot water and cook until fennel is soft.

Serve.

Butternut Puree

Ingredients

1 medium butternut squash

1 medium carrot

1 medium fennel

1 medium courgette

Pinch nutmeg

1 ½ liters hot water

¼ tsp pepper

Preparation

Chop butternut squash, carrot, fennel, and courgette.

Place all the ingredients in a saucepan and cover with the hot water. Bring to the boil, then simmer until the water almost evaporates.

Can be served as a side dish—mash or liquidize.

CURRY DISHES

Cauliflower Curry

Ingredients

1 tsp ghee

1 medium cauliflower, cut into florets

2 medium apples, chopped

1 tbs sultanas

2 medium carrots, diced

½ aubergine, chopped

2 tsp ground coriander

½ tsp ground cinnamon

2 tsp cumin

1 tsp ginger

1 cup coriander, fresh

1 cup boiling water

2 cups hot water

Salt & pepper to taste

Preparation

Fry cauliflower in the ghee for four minutes, stirring occasionally.

Add the water and remaining vegetables. Heat on high, stirring slowly until the water evaporates.

Stir in all the other ingredients. Add the hot water, simmer, and stir once or twice. Add more liquid if necessary.

Add the fresh coriander. Serve.

Vata, Pitta or Kapha Curry

Ingredients

1 apple

2-3 dates

1 tsp ginger

3 medium fennel bulbs

2 medium carrots, grated

1 celery stick

6 green beans

1 tsp turmeric

1 cup butternut squash

2 tsp churna (vata or pitta or kapha)

1 tsp cumin

1 tsp cardamom

1 liter boiling water

2 tsp ghee

Preparation

Chop the apple, dates, ginger, fennel, carrots, celery stick, and butternut squash.

Coat vegetables with the herbs and spices. Leave for ten to twenty minutes.

Heat the ghee and fry for two minutes, stirring continuously.

Add one cup of the boiling water and cook until the liquid evaporates. Add the remaining water and bring to the boil.

Simmer until the vegetables are cooked. Serve with rice.

Squash & Fennel Curry

Ingredients

1 tsp ghee

1 medium butternut squash

½ liter coconut milk

2 cups fennel

1 cup carrots

3 cups water

1 tsp cumin

1 tsp ground cardamom

1 tsp turmeric

1 tbs fresh coriander

1 tsp salt

Preparation

Chop the butternut squash, fennel, carrots, and fresh coriander.

Heat the ghee in a saucepan. Add the vegetables, herbs, and spices. Add some water and bring to the boil. Simmer for twenty-five minutes.

Add the coconut milk and simmer for a few minutes.

Add the coriander. Serve.

Sweet Korma

Ingredients

1 tsp ghee

½ red pepper

½ sweet apple

1 courgette

1 medium aubergine

½ cup dates

1 tsp grated ginger, fresh

1 tsp ground cardamom

¼ tsp nutmeg

½ cup raisins

2 tsp korma mix

1 cup coconut milk

water

Salt & pepper to taste

Preparation

Chop apple and dates. Slice red pepper and courgette. Cut the aubergine into cubes. Grate the nutmeg and ginger.

In a wok, melt the ghee. Add the red pepper and stir-fry for one minute.

Add half a cup of water and cook until the liquid evaporates.

Add the courgette and cook for one minute. Add the remaining ingredients and a quarter of a liter of water.

Bring to the boil, then lower the heat. Simmer until vegetables are cooked.

Add the coconut milk and simmer for another two minutes. Serve.

SOUPS

Carrot Soup

Serves four to six

All doshas can consume this soup. Pitta can feel the heat of carrots as well as ginger. Coconut brings cooling qualities to lessen the heat qualities of the ginger and carrots. The sweet tastes of the crystallized ginger and sugar also help in lessening the heat.

Ingredients

2 tbs butter

2 lbs carrots, peeled and chopped

2 small brown onions, chopped

4 cups water

½ tsp baking soda

¾ cups coconut milk, reduced fat

1 tbs grated ginger

¼ cup ginger, crystallized

1 tsp sugar

1 bunch cilantro

2 tsp salt

Salt & pepper to taste

Preparation

Chop and peel the carrots. Chop the onions and cilantro.

In a pot, heat the butter over medium heat until melted. Add the grated ginger, crystallized ginger, onion, and sugar. Cook for five to ten minutes until vegetables are softened.

Add the carrots, water, and baking soda. Bring to a simmer, cover, and lower the heat. Simmer for approximately twenty minutes or until carrots are tender.

Puree the soup in batches in a blender. Return the soup to the pot. Stir in the coconut milk. Cook over medium to low heat until the soup is hot.

Add salt and pepper to taste.

Sprinkle over the cilantro. Serve with chapatis for a light meal.

Corn Soup

Soup is usually served at midday and in the evenings, but corn soup is good for breakfast as well.

Corn soup is a balancer for the doshas, but for vata, the long-term effect is drying, so it can eat it occasionally. For pitta, only in moderation, and cilantro eliminates heat for pitta.

This is a good soup for weight loss as long as it is cooked without ghee. It is also good for people with high cholesterol.

Ingredients

5 corn cobs

5 cups water

¼ cup water

1 inch fresh ginger, peeled, chopped

1 tbs cilantro leaves, chopped

2 tbs ghee (except for the weight-loss version)

1 tsp cumin seeds

1 pinch salt

¼ tsp black pepper

Preparation

Wash corn and cut the corn off the cob to make four cups. Put the corn in a blender. Add two cups of water. Blend. Set aside in a bowl.

Blend cilantro, ginger, and a quarter of a cup of water for one minute until liquefied.

In a pot, add ghee and cumin and cook on medium heat. Add the blended spices, corn, and black pepper. When the seeds pop, add the remaining water and mix.

Boil gently for fifteen to twenty minutes until tender. Stir a few times. Add the salt and black pepper to taste.

Garnish with the cilantro leaves and serve.

TEAS

Vata Tea

½ tsp whole cumin

½ tsp coriander seeds

½ tsp fennel seeds

1 pinch whole-root licorice powder

3 pinches of ashwagandha root powder

Bring 1 liter of water to the boil. Add the spices and cover to steep.

Pour it into a thermos and drink throughout the day.

Drink at a warm temperature.

Pitta Tea

2 pinches of Indian Sarsaparilla powder

¼ tsp cumin

2 pinches of licorice powder

½ tsp fennel seeds

½ tsp coriander seeds

Boil 1 liter of water. Add spices and cover to steep.

Pour it into a thermos and drink throughout the day.

Drink at room temperature.

Kapha Tea

2 basil leaves

2 thin slices of fresh ginger root

2 whole cloves

½ tsp whole cumin seeds

2 pinches licorice powder

Boil 1 liter of water. Add spices and cover to steep.

Pour it into a thermos and drink throughout the day.

Drink at warm to hot temperatures.

Sip during and after meals.

Detoxifying Tea

¼ tsp whole cumin

½ tsp whole fennel

½ tsp whole coriander

Boil 1 liter of water. Add spices and allow to steep for ten minutes. Cover.

Strain the spices and pour water into a thermos.

Sip throughout the day.

HOMEMADE VEGETABLE AND FRUIT JUICES

These homemade juices are wonderful for the tastebuds and a restorative tonic for the body. They contain an abundance of antioxidants, vitamins, nutritional enzymes, and minerals easily digested by the body. One or two pints of juice each day can be consumed, but juices that have raw/cooked fruits and vegetables should also be a part of a daily diet. These juices help to cleanse the colon and keep the digestive system functioning properly.

Vata Balancing Juices

Beetroot, carrot, cucumber (headaches and weight loss)

Apple (headaches, asthma, and arthritis)

Lemon and ginger (migraines)

Apple, guava, and potato (insomnia)

Beetroot (gaining weight and a liver cleanser)

Grape (good for rheumatism, dry skin, and constipation)

Apricot, orange, cranberry, peach, pomegranate, pineapple (different combination)

Carrot, asparagus, cucumber, turnip, green beans, pumpkin (different combinations)

Pitta Balancing Juices

Carrot, ginger (eyes)

Carrot, spinach (purifies the blood, good for weight loss)

Watermelon (refreshing and cooling)

Pineapple, peach, pomegranate, apple, prunes, grapes (different combinations)

Celery, asparagus, potato, cucumber, leek, peas, cabbage (different combinations)

Kapha Balancing Juices

Grape (constipation)

Carrot, cucumber, celery (weight loss)

Orange, papaya, pomegranate (reduces constipation)

Apples, berries, pears, cherries, peaches, mangoes, prunes (different combinations)

Carrot, asparagus, potato, spinach, celery (different combinations)

OTHER DRINKS AND DIGESTIVES

Hot water

Hot water reduces impurities and toxicity in the tissues, is good for weight loss and digestion, and balances the physiology of all body types. It is also a general cleanser and purifier of the body.

Boil water, preferably distilled, and then pour into a container.

Take small sips throughout the day.

Add lemon, fresh ginger or peppermint for extra flavor if desired.

Nourishing Milk Drink

1 cup organic milk

8 -10 raisins

2 tsp root ginger

Pinch of turmeric

Pinch of cardamom

½ tsp ghee

½ inch vanilla pod

Pinch nutmeg

Place ingredients (except for the ghee) in a saucepan. Bring to a boil slowly, then simmer for two minutes, stirring continuously. Add the ghee. Pour into a cup and drink.

Rice milk or soy may be used for lactose intolerance. Boiling milk breaks down the proteins, making it much easier to digest and causing less mucus and congestion than drinking cold milk.

It should not be taken with meals but alone for breakfast and/or before bedtime.

According to Ayurveda, milk is rejuvenating, strengthening, and nourishing. It soothes the mind and promotes longevity. It is high in calcium and has been shown to reduce cholesterol levels. People diagnosed with lactose intolerance can digest small quantities of boiled milk, especially once the above ingredients are added.

Ginger pickle

½ tsp grated ginger

½ tsp lemon juice, freshly squeezed

½ tsp honey, cold pressed/organic

Pinch of salt

The ingredients are enough for one serving but more convenient to make a week's supply at a time. To do this, grate the fresh ginger to fill half a jam jar, cover with lemon juice, and store in a refrigerator. Twenty minutes before lunch or an evening meal take one teaspoon of the ginger/lemon mix, add honey (to taste), and a pinch of salt.

Taking ginger pickle regularly helps maintain strong, healthy digestion. It improves the assimilation and metabolism of nutrients from the food you eat.

From an Ayurvedic standpoint, it contains all six tastes (sweet, sour, salty, bitter, pungent, and astringent) required to satisfy the palate. The body will feel balanced and satisfied.

Date Recipe

Soak ten to fifteen dates overnight. In a saucepan, cook for ten-fifteen minutes. Remove the pits, then blend with one teaspoon of ghee and a pinch of cardamom.

Good with breakfast or as a pick-me-up in the afternoon.

Summary

There is so much in the practice of Ayurveda that is good, positive, and healthy for our mind, body, and spirit. Each chapter of this book has shown us how we benefit from the different elements that comprise the Ayurvedic lifestyle.

Every element of Ayurveda is unto itself intertwined with one another. We find how our total being is cared for, not just the superficial or a portion of it. At times we may take this for granted.

Ayurveda allows us to take hold of how we manage ourselves each day. If we are stressed, all the elements of Ayurveda address the stress or anxiety that we deal with in our lives. If we have an illness or disease, we can manage it with Ayurvedic herbs and medicine.

For many, Ayurveda is becoming an alternative to the pills and medications that conventional medicine uses to treat the illness that has already manifested and at an expense that has become unreachable. People are looking more to prevent diseases from occurring or treat better and maintain one that has already taken hold. This is why this medical system is becoming more of a choice.

If we are faced with a hectic daily life, we can find comfort in meditation or yoga to put space between us and the chaos of our world. There might be an event that has caused sadness that may be difficult to address, and Ayurveda can help ease the feelings we are struggling with and help us get through it.

Meditation, yoga, and aromatherapy are interlinked and help to bring health as well as calmness. Just the thought of having a few minutes of serenity and space to enjoy a massage, inhale exhilarating or soothing fragrances, stretch the body, and release any tension seems a perfect way to treat our body, mind, and health.

We can be healed by the properties of herbs and essential oils of Ayurveda. Each can reduce inflammation, stress, and treat certain diseases. As we age, it is imperative to protect our body from disease and harm. Practicing yoga, using natural remedies, and becoming knowledgeable about how you can maintain a high level of health is invaluable for your health and wellbeing.

With Ayurveda, we can understand better who we are and know our dosha, constitution, and learn how best to eat and what type of foods to avoid. And for those of us who struggle with our weight, this is a perfect way to truly understand why our body does not respond as we would like it to when it comes to losing the stubborn weight. Finding natural ways to lose weight through diet, mental and physical stimulation, and seeking calmness can actually help.

Millions of people worldwide practice Ayurveda for their health. They have mental stability, as well as the calmness and peace it provides. Hopefully, you have a fuller understanding of Ayurvedic medicine, its longevity as a medical system, and the positive lifestyle it can offer. You can now go on to share the beautiful world that is Ayurveda with the people you care for the most.

Namaste.

Conclusion

Thank you for reading *Unlocking the Secrets of Hindu Healing Through the Ayurveda Diet, Yoga, Aromatherapy, and Meditation*. It should have been informative and provided you with all the information you need to understand the practice of Ayurveda and the health benefits it can provide.

Based on the belief that health can be attained by creating a balance of mind, body, and spirit, Ayurveda is the science that is a sister of yoga. Our personal health can be changed through our awareness of our environments. The foundation of health is attaining the balance of mind and body.

Ayurveda is a beautiful practice that provides peace, health, and wellbeing. It is a lifestyle that might, in the beginning, be a shift to the way you have thought or lived, but adopting even portions of Ayurveda is a wonderful way to be good to yourself and, in turn, be good to others.

Reading this book should have enlightened you to the many facets of Ayurveda and what we need to bring our mind, body, and spirit into balance. Yoga, meditation, and aromatherapy are some of the elements of the Ayurvedic lifestyle.

The next step is to identify the needs of your mind, body, and spirit and use this book as a guide to achieving the symmetry that Ayurveda strives to teach and provide.

Use the information found in this book to create a master plan and embrace the practice of Ayurveda. Incorporate the healing elements into your life and embrace the peace and wellbeing Ayurveda provides.

Part 2: Yoga Sutras

An Essential Guide to Understanding the
Yoga Sutras of Patanjali

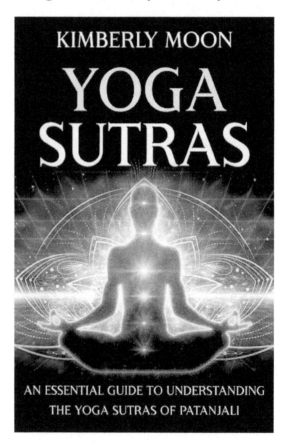

Introduction

Let's play a game. I will ask a cliché question. You have only to give two answers. One now and the other at the end of this introduction, right before you delve deeper into this book's chapters. My question is simple. Are you happy?

Say things turned out the way they should, you snagged that promotion, made partner, or your check is fatter than it used to be a year ago. Or maybe your relationship is going well (or you found your feet after a toxic partnership fell flat), and your body mass index is ideal, you would say yes, wouldn't you?

What if I told you that absent these things, you could still be happy? Say the coin was flipped and you had less than a dollar to your name. Say your weighed down by student loans, or you've lost a loved one, or you're terrified of looking at your reflection in the mirror for fear you won't like what you see. It's crazy to think you'd still be happy, right?

In life, we depend on a lot of external factors for happiness. These factors are temporary and are as unpredictable as the stock market. Because of our lack of awareness, we live our lives trapped in a rat race for success, happiness, and all other means of gratification, most of which aren't personally defined by us. While we exist instead of living, life ebbs away. We search endlessly for the next trip, forgetting there is a path to bliss — one that isn't short-lived — a course full of purpose, joy, and meaning regardless of life's circumstances.

Yoga is a tested and trusted practice, not just for health and flexibility (although that is a bonus), but for personal development and spiritual awakening. A compilation of 196 aphorisms known as sutras contain lessons put together over two thousand years ago by a sage named Patañjali (पतञ्जल).

These sutras are divided into four chapters, each outlining nuggets of spiritual wisdom, some of which have clear cut lessons. In contrast, others are more complex with a slightly different meaning depending on who you ask. All chapters were treated in this book. The lessons in each chapter are kept simple without drifting away from the original content and underlying message.

I can guarantee you a fun, inspiring read. Yoga does more than make you sweat, breathe easier, and have you shopping for trendy sportswear. Practice yoga long enough, and you gain certain superpowers — none of which are to be used selfishly, I warn. Some other things you will learn in this text include but are not limited to:

- How to find your center, so you don't experience life like a kite at the mercy of the winds;

- How to become attuned to the subtle language of your body, because like it or not, your body communicates with you more often than you realize;

- How to improve your levels of concentration and silence the inner ramblings of your mind;

- How to observe and react objectively, guiding your perception towards that which is fair and trustworthy.

Do I have your attention now? How badly do you want to turn the page? Before you do so, I ask again: Are you happy? If you are, then read this just for kicks. Read it for the same reason if you are undecided. You may just discover happiness in one (or all) of these pages. I hope you stay enthralled until you get to the end of the very last chapter. Namaste!

Chapter One: Introduction to Yoga Philosophy

Humble Origins

The word "Yoga" originated from the Sanskrit word "Yuj," which means "to unite," "to yoke," or "to join." In Yogic scripture, practicing yoga initiates a harmony or equilibrium between individual awareness and universal consciousness, leading to a perfect balance between the body, mind, man, and nature.

This harmony of existence defines the integration of human persona at the highest level, which is why genuine yoga practitioners are said to have reached a frame of mind known as "Nirvana," "Mukti," or "Moksha," all of which are states of emancipation or release.

Yoga is a psychosomatic spiritual instruction focused on health, harmony, and overcoming all states of human suffering and pain to regain mastery of our destiny. Maharishi Patanjali describes yoga as the art of suppressing the modifications of the human mind to attain complete self-realization.

The Philosophy of Yoga

In Indian culture, the word for philosophy is "Darśana," from the Sanskrit word "Drish," meaning "to experience or see." Yoga is a spiritual practice entrenched in ancient Indian wisdom, thought, and life. Yogi darśanas instruct us to see life as it is, living life so the equilibrium of mind and body easily comprehends the truth. The six yoga philosophies are intertwined with each other to form an impressive philosophical system known as the Shad Darśana, and they are:

1. **Nyāya or Judgment or Logic (Sanskrit न्याय):** The sage Aksapada Gautama was a proponent of yoga from a multidimensional perspective, one which lends itself to logic and holds up the ideals of the right practices, rules, and judgment. There are four ways to get knowledge:

- Through inference, or Anumāna (Sanskrit: अनु),

- Through testimony or word, also known as Śabda (Sanskrit: शब्द)

- Through evidence and observation, or Pratyakṣa (Sanskrit: प्रत्यक्ष), and

- Through comparison or resemblance, or Upamāna (Sanskrit: उपमान).

2. **Sānkhya (Sanskrit सांख्य), the study of the physical universe also known as cosmology:** The sage Kapila founded this philosophy. It offers a foundation for all levels of manifestation, no matter how small or large. The word Sānkhya originates from the Sanskrit word "Samyag Akhyate," which means "that which explains or foretells the whole."

- Sānkhya also involves Ahaṃkāra (अहंकार meaning ego or pride)

- Prakṛti (energy, potency, source or nature)

- Purusha (Sanskrit: Puruṣa पुरुष meaning spirit, consciousness, or self), buddhi (intellect or the ability to discern)

- Manas (sixth sense)

- The three Gunas: Tamas (darkness, death or destruction); Sattva (purity, goodness, and light); and Rajas (birth, passion or energy)

- The Indriyas or sensory faculties which include the five Jnanendriya or wisdom senses (Chaksu-eyes, Shotra- ears, Jiva- tongue, Tvak- skin, and Grahnu- nose)

- The five Karmendriyas (action or means of expression such as Vak (the mouth to proclaim), Payu (the rectum to eliminate), Pani (the hands to grasp), Upgastha (the genitals to procreate), and Pada (the feet to move)

- The five elements: Vayu (air), Prithvi (earth), Jala (water), Akasha (ether), and Agni (fire).

3. **Pūrva Mīmāṃsā or Mīmāṃsā (Sanskrit मीमांसा), revered thought, reflection, or critical investigation:** Sage Rishi Jaimini was the founder of this philosophy, firmly emphasizing the importance of profound intuition. Moksha, or enlightenment, can be achieved through worship, ritual, and/or ethics. This is the philosophy that later became the philosophy of karma (Sanskrit: कर्म) or cause and effect.

4. **Vaiśeṣika or Vaisheshika (Sanskrit वैशेषिक), scientific observation:** Kanada Kashyapa first propounded this philosophy around the 2nd century. Later on, the renowned Praśastapāda, philosopher and writer of the ancient

Collection of Properties of Matter or Padārtha-dharma-saṅgraha developed this philosophy further. It emphasizes the importance of chemistry, physics, physical sciences, and the five elements.

5. **Vedānta (Sanskrit: वेदान्त), the end of the Vedas)** In the 7th century, the philosopher Gaudapada created this philosophy, which was later developed in the 8th century by Adi Shankara. This school of thought teaches methods of self-realization beyond death, decomposition, or decay. One of the fundamental tenets in Vedanta philosophy is Mahāvākyas (the great sayings of ancient texts used in meditation). This philosophy was described in the writings of the Upanishads. The poem Vivekachudamani (Sanskrit विवेकचूडामणि) by Adi Shankara is a wonderful demonstration of the Vedanta philosophy.

6. **Yoga (Sanskrit: योग, meaning effort, union, or introspection):** Apart from being a spiritual exercise, yoga is also a philosophy. The philosophy of yoga is closely related to the Sānkhya ideology. The only difference is that yoga believes in the existence of God or gods and depends on only three out of six proofs of knowledge (prāmaṇas), namely Anumāna or inference, Pratyakṣa or perception, and Āptavacana/ Śabda or testimony.

Forms of Yoga

There are many forms of yoga, each with its unique character and focus, and they are:

Karma Yoga: This is also called Karma marga and is known as the yoga of action. Karma yoga aims to establish a life devoid of negativity, ego, and selfishness.

Jñāna Yoga: This form of yoga is dedicated to acquiring wisdom through study.

Rāja Yoga: Formerly called Aṣṭāṅga yoga or classical yoga, the form of yoga aligns closely with the yoga sutras from Patanjali. In ancient Sanskrit texts, it is the highest form of yoga guaranteed to grant Samadhi or enlightenment via mediation and a form adherence to the eight limbs of yoga (which I will get to later in this book).

Hatha Yoga: This is a physical and mental path of yoga created to increase the strength of the mind and body.

Bhakti Yoga: This is about unconditional devotion to God and the undeniable importance of purity (Sattva). It's about finding the best ways to direct emotions, grow in patience, tolerance, and understanding.

Tantra Yoga: The word tantra comes from the Sanskrit term तन्त्र, meaning "to loop, wrap, or weave." It is a combination of rituals, ceremonies, or texts used as a vehicle to foster Siddhi (completion, bliss, strength, and clarity of thought) in day to day living.

The Spread of Yoga

The practice of yoga began in the Indus-Sarasvati civilization of northern India as far back as 5,000 years ago. However, researchers argue that yoga dates to as far as 10,000 years when sacred texts written out on flimsy palm leaves suffered loss or damage.

Yogic mythology proclaims Lord Shiva as the Adi yogi (the first yogi) or guru. Thousands of years ago, on the bank of the Kantisarovar lake in the Himalayas, Shiva poured his knowledge into the seven sages known as the Saptarishi.

These sages spread the science of yoga to different ends of the earth, from Africa and South America to Asia and the Middle East.

Although parallels in its expression can be found in diverse ancient cultures, it was in India that yoga's science discovered its full capacity. Agastya, one of the seven Saptarishi, traveled across the Indian subcontinent, establishing yogi culture and way of life.

The Phases of Yoga in History

The Pre-Classical Phase: This phase was the period of the spread of yoga in the Indus-Sarasvati civilization. The Rigveda was composed between 1500 and 1200 BC by members of the early Kuru tribe, which served as the center of Vedic civilization. They were in the northwest of Punjab, presently known as Uttar Pradesh. Rigveda is derived from the word Rig, which means verse or praise, and Veda, which means knowledge. The Rigveda is one of the most sacred and the most ancient of canonical texts, in which you'll find 10,600 verses and 1,028 poems, all of which are systematized into ten mandalas, or circles. It contains the Samhitas, Aranyakas, Brahmanas, and Upanishads, but the Samhita is the core text. Battle hymns, divine invocations, spells, narrative dialogues, and ritual observations popularly used by the Aryans (nobles) who migrated to India from Iran are a part of Rigveda's contents.

The practice of yoga was refined over time after the Aryans, thanks to mystic seers and practitioners known as Rishis and Brahmans. These practitioners noted down their treasured practices and beliefs into what we now call the Upanishads.

The Rigveda may be the most ancient yogi text; still, the most celebrated remains the Bhagavad-Gītā (also known as the celestial or divine song) written around the year 500 BC. It is the conversation between the God Krishna and Arjuna (a Pandava warrior). Like the Rigveda, the Bhagavad-Gītā also teaches morals and religious beliefs. The Upanishads documented the practice of ego sacrifice via wisdom (jnana yoga), self-realization, and action (karma yoga).

The Classical Phase: Yoga progressed from being a patchwork of belief systems and ideas at war with each other. The highlight of the classical period is the introduction of Patanjali's yoga sutras in the second century. In his text, the exact path of the raja or classical yoga is explained and arranged into eight paths or limbs, with each stage closer to obtaining enlightenment or Samadhi.

The Post-Classical Phase: Many centuries after Patanjali, other yoga masters fashioned practices and exercises dedicated to physical rejuvenation and life extension. These new doctrines did not abide by the ancient Vedic texts; instead, they upheld the physical body's role as the gateway to enlightenment.

This led to tantra yoga's popularity, which boasted unusual yet effective techniques to purify the body and mind from the ropes of our physical existence. Exploring these techniques of the mind-body connection led to Hatha yoga, which is now the Western world's most popular form of yoga.

Modern Yoga: Between the late 1800s and early 1900s, yoga masters traveled to the West, bringing attention to yoga's benefits and garnering more followers. The first step in this process happened in the Parliament of Religions, Chicago, in 1893, following Swami Vivekananda's outstanding lecture on yoga practices and the universality of religions.

Soon after, Hatha yoga was introduced by Tirumalai Krishnamacharya, an Indian scholar, teacher, and Ayurvedic healer who later founded the Hatha Yoga School in Mysore, India in 1924. Sivananda created the Divine Life Society on the banks of the Ganges river in 1936. T. Krishnamacharya taught three students who later carried his legacy of Hatha yoga: T.K.V. Desikachar, Pattabhi Jois, and the popular B.K.S Iyengar. In 1947, Indra Devi (Eugenie Peterson) opened the first Hollywood yoga studio at 8806 Sunset Boulevard.

Sri Patanjali's Philosophy and His Contribution to Yoga

Sri Patanjali, also called Gonikaputra or Gonardiya, was an enigma. Little or no details exist about the life of the legend said to be the very epitome of yoga. Historians believe he was born in the 2nd century BC to Gonika, a virtuous yogini (female yoga practitioner), and he's said to be the reincarnation of the thousand-headed serpent god Ananta Shesha. This is the reason Patanjali is often depicted as half-human, half serpent.

Some people claim Patanjali was a lawyer, others say he was a physician, while a few say he was a grammarian. It is crucial to clear up this misconception. The Patanjali credited with writing the yoga sutras differs from the one responsible for the commentary on Panini's grammar. Patanjali is said to be the father of yoga, but it is clear that he was not its creator. He is only seen as the epitome of yoga because he was an accomplished teacher who understood suffering and had mapped out a practical step-by-step guide to alleviate it. Sri Patanjali codified yoga teachings into 196 aphorisms or sutras.

The word "Sutra" in Sanskrit means "string;" hence, every aphorism or declaration is similar to a lone flower in a garland. This codification of yoga teachings made it easy to understand and pass on, unlike the old oral yoga instruction technique.

The yoga philosophy by Patanjali is mostly dualistic. What this means is both the divine or Prakriti and the human or Purusha exist alongside each other, but they still maintain their separation, being completely different entities. In other words, everything in this world is entirely made of matter and spirit.

The Categories of Patanjali's Sutras

The whole point of yoga is to set us free from the stronghold of the world of matter and bring us closer and closer to the cosmos until we become one with the All. Patanjali's 196 sutras educate us on self-discovery and the importance of understanding one's place in the universe. His sutras fall into four main categories, each with its unique purpose and focus:

- Kaivalya Pada (freedom from agony or affliction)
- Samadhi Pada (specifying what yoga and awareness is)
- Vibhuti Pada (diligence in the practice of discipline)
- Sadhana Pada (the link between the yogi and higher consciousness)

The sutras are far from direct answers as they lack concise or universal meanings. They are a guide or compass for the yogi to understand that each earthly or spiritual experience is unique, and everyone will have their lessons to learn on the path of self-realization.

To Sri Patanjali, the pain and heartache is part of the process. Like every journey, as you reach the peak of true self-discovery, the pain fades away. Following the sutras' organization by Patanjali, the teachings soon became popular and were translated to at least 42 languages, including Arabic and old Japanese. Patanjali's teachings lost their popularity in the 19th century for 700 years until Swami Vivekananda, other yoga masters, and the Theosophical Society revived them.

The Relevance of Yoga in the Present Century

With the discovery of neuroplasticity, science has confirmed the efficacy of ancient yogi practices, including meditation, mental

Sanskaras (recollections or physiological imprint), and Asanas (poses) in strengthening the neural pathways and improving physical, mental, emotional, and social health. Carl Gustav Jung, the famous Swiss psychiatrist and psychologist, described yoga as one of the greatest inventions of the human mind.

Science and the burden of the 21st century may have dominated our style of living, making us dependent on technology, encouraging chaos and stress, limiting our lifespans, and weakening our bodies, rendering us prone to the mental and physical malaise. Yoga, however, is one spiritual exercise that provides a lasting solution to these stressors, allowing a balance in both mind and body. The 21st of June is celebrated worldwide as World Yoga Day - and for a good reason. Let's delve into the benefits of practicing yoga.

Physical Benefits of Yoga

1. Increased Circulatory and Cardiovascular Health: Evidence exists that yoga reduces heart disease by 30 percent and mortality following cardiac arrest by 48 percent.

2. Improved Immunity, Vitality, and Slower Aging: Regular yoga and meditation benefit the telomeres, which are the chromosomes responsible for keeping the cells in prime health. In the process, it increases your resistance to disease. Yoga also gives you glowing skin.

3. Cancer Care: Transcendental meditation and yoga are helpful in cancer therapy. The fact that yoga is available, affordable, and non-invasive is a bonus, too.

4. Better Blood Pressure: Yoga reduces blood pressure and prevents ailments such as kidney malfunction, artery damage, and heart failure.

5. Improved Body Posture: Asanas help strengthen muscles, aid them to better support the body's weight. Yoga poses can correct lumbar lordosis (back pain), kyphosis or scoliosis (abnormal curvature of the spine), and atrophy (muscle wasting because of lack of use).

The Mental Benefits of Yoga

The advantages of yoga on our mental health are diverse, and it has been labeled a vital tool in the practice of psychotherapy by the American Psychological Association. Benefits include:

1. Better Moods: Yoga increases GABA levels. GABA (Gamma Amino Butyric Acid) is a chemical messenger in the brain that controls fear and anxiety. Regulation of GABA prevents burnout and depression as the brain releases feel-good chemicals after each yoga session. All that oxytocin, serotonin, and dopamine levels skyrocket to make you feel like you are walking on sunshine. Stress hormones like cortisol also drastically decrease.

2. Improved Rest and Recreation: Yoga also improves the condition of your parasympathetic nervous system (also called the rest and digest system). When the PNS is in synergy, your digestion and bowel movements improve. You sleep better, you have no problems getting aroused, and you have an even bigger chance of achieving "the big O" during intimacy.

3. Care for Autism Spectrum Disorders: Yoga helps calm the mind holistically and naturally. Instead of pills and syringes, practicing yoga quells the usual temper tantrums thrown by autistic patients and allows them to adjust their personalities to the world around them.

4. Addiction Control: Transcendental meditation is one of the easy ways to battle addiction, be it food, sex, drugs, or alcohol. With constant practice, students learn to build abstinence to these damaging habits. A study by Moliver in

2011 on obese women over 45 shows how yoga was effective in reducing their body mass index and food consumption.

5. Pain Reduction and Management: Regular yoga affects the parietal lobe of the brain. This part is responsible for speech, limb movements, and pain. Studies conducted in 2011 demonstrated the efficacy of yoga following mindfulness and meditation for as little as two months in reducing pain sensitivity.

6. Better Information Processing: Our brains have cortical infoldings known as sulci and gyri. These folds house several neurons responsible for advanced functions such as keeping up with your boss's ever-changing demands each second and planning for the future.

Yoga increases the surface areas of your brain's cortical folds, improving memory and cognitive performance. Yoga can also make you smarter and more self-aware by increasing the size of the hippocampus and the somatosensory cortex. These two areas are responsible for anxiety control and self-awareness, respectively. Thus, regular yoga leads to increased lucidity, self-confidence, and improved self-esteem.

The Emotional and Social Benefits of Yoga

Meditation and yoga help us better express our feelings and temper our responses in stressful situations. As humans, we will not always have control over how we feel, but yoga can teach us how to react by suppressing our basal or banal instincts. Practicing yoga also increases our appreciation for the world around us. This helps us accept responsibility for our environment so we can play our part in creating a better world.

Chapter Two: Background of Yoga Sutras — Important Concepts

The Concept of Vritti

Vritti (Sanskrit वृत्ति) is a very ancient word that describes consciousness as a vortex. Think of a whirlpool made of thought, or the never-ending chatter that goes on in your mind, with no clear beginning and no end in sight, and you'll have a fair view of what vritti is. In Patanjali's yoga sutras, it is written, "Yogas citta vritti ni rodha," which translates to "Yoga is the neutralization of the vortices of feeling."

The concept of vritti represents attachments and egoistic desires. According to Patañjali, yoga aims to neutralize such whirlpools or egoistic desires by stabilizing the spinal center. For example, base desires such as lust are located along the lower chakras such as the root and sacral chakra, all of which are the seats of emotional and physical identity connecting your image and keeping you grounded in the world.

Vritti is born in your subconscious mind, or your memory, or Citta. It's not something that comes up on its own, as it's the side effect of being deluded, holding on to misconceptions, or choosing to be blind to the true reality. This delusion is known as Avidyā (Sanskrit अविद्या). The only way to destroy this ignorance or delusion (avidya) is by acquiring Jñāna (spiritual knowledge). Upon the destruction of avidya, vritti moves on to become the universal principle or absolute reality, also known as Brahman (Sanskrit ब्रह्मन्; Hindi ब्रह्म). This step of controlling vritti is essential because thought patterns function to cause Avarana-Bhanga, which removes the veil of Sthula Avidya (the veil of ignorance) in our reality.

Besides representing mental awareness, vritti can be a catchphrase for thoughts experienced while awake, asleep, or in any altered state of awareness. Vritti could also mean the mind's capacity to express feelings such as like or dislike, need, contentment, etc. In Hindu and Vedic texts, samskaras are mental recollections, habitual thought patterns, or psychological imprints of past actions.

In this vein, samskaras serve as a foundation for karma (the spiritual principle of cause and effect). Like potholes or tire tracks on the road, the implications of samskaras develop into vritti that shape our behaviors and thought patterns and complexes that make each individual special.

The expression of vritti can be positive or negative. The base of the vritti of love is also called Mamata. This is in the heart. Fear (Bhaya) is in the stomach. We can see these sensations when one sees red while angry or develops a feeling of butterflies while in love. It is essential to understand that positive vritti can quickly grow into negative expressions. For example, when overexpressed, fear can lead to cowardice, and love could lead to jealousy or overprotective behavior.

The practice of yoga is not to eliminate or suppress vritti, but to control it, find a balance, and learn to channel these tendencies inward positively. For instance, during meditation, one can dissolve their vritti and direct them through the spine to the third eye or brow chakra between the eyebrows. This channeling of thoughts dispels egomania, like or dislike, and allows one to reach a higher state of consciousness.

Vritti and Chakras

Some vritti linked with various focal points or chakra include:

The Muladhara (Root Chakra): This is the seat of bliss in concentration, immense joy, pleasure, and passion.

The Swadhisthana (Sacral Chakra): This is associated with intimacy, sensuality and creativity, and pleasure. This channel is blocked by fear and is the seat of suspicion, destructiveness, affection, ignorance, and contempt.

The Manipura (Solar Plexus Chakra): This is associated with thirst, envy, shame, fear, sadness, spiritual ignorance, and deceit.

The Anahata (Heart Chakra): This is the energy center of calm, balance, and serenity. It is the base of lascivious behavior, indecision, hope, arrogance, discrimination, obstinacy, fraudulent behavior, longing, and anxiety.

The Vishuddha (Throat Chakra): This houses feelings of purity, speech, and calm.

The Ajna (Brow Chakra): This is also called the third eye chakra, and signifies the subconscious mind. Closely associated with the brain, it is the center of pure spiritual energy.

The Sahasrara (Crown Chakra): This is the chakra of prayer and intimate relationship with the cosmos. It gives man the leeway to higher states of consciousness or awareness.

Types of Vritti

In Sutra 1.2, Patañjali states, "योगश्चित्तवृत्तिनिरोध" or "yogaś-citta-vṛtti-nirodhaḥ." This verse means that yoga is the nirodha (process of terminating) vritti (definitions) of citta (mind-stuff or field of consciousness). The five main types of vritti or thought whirlpools affecting our consciousness are:

1. **Feeling, Fantasy, Imagination or Vikalpa (Sanskrit: विकल्प).** This whirlpool of thought is not a consequence of inference or discernment, but a product of words and concepts devoid of meaning. For instance, the noun time is far from an object. Time is infinite, but in our minds, time creates an image based on thoughts. We measure this concept in seconds, minutes, days, or even years. Other abstract nouns in this category include peace, love, hatred, and so on.

2. **Sleep or Nidra (Sanskrit: निद्रा).** Deep sleep or rest is a vritti characterized by the absence of mental content. It is considered vritti because you can admit to enjoying a good sleep after a long day or not having enough sleep. Rest is an experience where human consciousness can remain alert while remaining in your memory as a label, one that when you wake translates into an experience.

3. **Right knowledge or Prāmaṇa (Sanskrit: प्रमाण).** Perception, in this case, is determined using the testimony of mouth (agamah), direct cognition or perception (pratyakṣa), and inference or deduction (anumāna).

4. **Misconception or Delusion or Viparyaya (Sanskrit: विपर्यय).** Viparyaya is a Sanskrit word meaning reversal, non-existence, or misapprehension. This vritti is a thought pattern born out of the human mind's machinations and can be disputed or nullified with evidence, enlightenment, or the

right perception. Viparyaya is the darkness that clouds the mind, preventing it from distinguishing between fallacy and reality.

5. Memory or Smriti (Sanskrit: स्मृति). This is the consequence of all the other vrittis. Memory signifies the refusal to let go of an experience, subject, image, or object. Like the other vritti, memories and impressions can be painful or pleasurable. Each memory creates samskara (imprints) in mind, manifesting as a recollection of a memory. Each new image, object, subject, or occurrence acts as a catalyst that activates other stored experiences and may cause pain or pleasure depending on what recollection it triggered.

According to Patañjali, yoga trains us to differentiate between thought patterns, discover prāmaṇa, and acknowledge the vritti. Doing this may sound easy in theory, but is a task easier said than achieved.

The Metaphysical Schools of Thought

There are three metaphysical schools of thought or Darshana, all slightly distinct from one another, and all expounding upon the same truth through different lenses, complementing one another in the process. They are:

- Dvaita Vedānta or dualism
- Advaita Vedānta or non-dualism
- Viśiṣṭādvaita or qualified non-dualism

Dvaita Vedānta (Sanskrit: द्वैत वेदान्त)

Dualism or Dvaita is the foundation of Patañjali's yoga sutras. In dualism, it is believed that puruṣa (पुरुष – pure consciousness, soul or the cosmos) and Prakṛiti (प्रकृति – nature, primal matter or the constantly evolving matrix of the universe) coexist in harmony and an everlasting attraction with each other.

Prakṛiti itself comprises three Gunas (qualities or modes of existence): Sattva (illumination), tamas (inertia), and rajas (movement). When the attraction between prakṛiti and puruṣa become overwhelming, it leads to one merging into the other, disrupting the equilibrium maintained between the three gunas. In dualism, we aim to liberate ourselves from this dependency on prakṛiti, transcending above our ego to attain liberation (mokṣa) and our true self (puruṣa).

Dualism proposes the existence of the two independent principles of matter and spirit. The two are far from being equal, with matter being subservient to spirit. Dualism implies that our mind is more than the organ called the brain. This idea exists because, with Dvaita, our minds possess consciousness, a non-material and spiritual aspect with an eternal attribute.

Advaita Vedānta (Sanskrit: अद्वैत वेदान्त)

Advaita has Sanskrit roots translating to "A Dvaita" — two. Advaita means non-dualism. It was initially known as Puruṣavāda or Māyāvāda. It is a famous school of Hindu and Vedanta philosophy, which proposes that the soul is one with the Brahman.

This philosophy is the foundation of the Bhagavad-Gītā. The father of Advaita is Adi Shankara, a theologian and philosopher (788-820 AD). The gospel of Advaita, however, started initially with the Upanishads and later spread helped by Gauḍapāda, a medieval era Hindu philosopher and scholar, and Govinda Bhagavatpāda, the student of Gauḍapāda who later became the guru of Adi Shankara.

Shankara himself had four prominent students: Padmapāda, Hastamalaka, Toṭaka, and Sureśvara. Advaita is both a philosophy and an experience. As an experience, it is the pinnacle of spirituality a human can attain. This is a philosophy that helps us understand how humans are connected to the absolute or the Brahman.

In Advaita, there is only one reality. The Brahman and Nirvana or liberation is attained not through belief but via experience (Anubhava, Sanskrit: अनुभव).

The Brahman is pure bliss, a state of pure consciousness and supreme reality. It is the fundamental truth behind all experiences and objects. Absolute Brahman is Nirguṇa (without form or qualities) while Saguṇa Brahman — सगुण — is Brahman with qualities experienced as a deity known as Īśvara. Īśvara is an essential concept in Advaita as it represents two things: The infinite cosmic intelligence and the all-pervading omniscient and universal God.

Īśvara is the totality of the continually evolving multifold universe. In Advaita, the individual (atman) is the microcosm embedded in Īśvara (the macrocosm), which possesses limitless space, time, and causation with endless boundaries, possibilities, and potency.

Think of Brahman (Avivarta) as a frame upon which the whole universe sits; you can't quite refer to the world as being real or unreal. The trouble with the human mind is that it is ever plagued by a very persistent illusion (Māyā), which wants to be perceived as real. It also contends with ignorance (Avidyā). The illusion, coupled with ignorance, causes us to perceive reality through a funhouse mirror, with so many distortions; this causes us to live life in such a way we create the worst of karmic impressions and remain stuck in the never-ending cycle of cause and effect.

Advaita's firmest belief about karma is that the whole reason for its existence is to purify our minds from such concepts as likes and dislikes, or (Raga dveṣa vimuktah). If we can rid ourselves of māyā, we will embrace our true nature, wake up from the cosmic dream called life, free ourselves from karmic bondage and live in eternal bliss. Shankara believed that the world was full of illusion, and beneath everything is Brahman.

The Development of Advaita Philosophy

Developing this profound Advaita philosophy took place in four stages. Let's take a look at each one.

The Upanishad Era: Here, the Advaita philosophy was more of a hypothesis. It passes its lessons via word of mouth from one generation to the next.

The Shankara Era: The 8th century saw Adi Shankara conceptualizing Advaita and establishing Brahman's non-dualism as the ultimate reality. Concepts such as māyā and ajñāna were introduced to explain better the creation and presence of duality in the universe, one that did not affect the non-dual nature of Brahman.

The Post-Shankara Era: This was the most extended period lasting from the 9th to the 16th century. Philosophers such as Madhusudana, Padmapāda, Vachaspati, Vimuktatman, Sarvajñatman, and Sureshwara characterized this period.

This period marked Advaita's division into three schools: the Virana school founded on the views of Padmapāda and Prakashatman, the Vartika school from the beliefs of Sureshwara; and the Bhamati school on the premise of Vachaspati Mishra. These schools refined the philosophy of Advaita by shifting the focus from Brahman to māyā. The four principles that propounded in this era include:

- Dual or two-level reality
- Non-duality of consciousness
- The illusion of Jivatva or individuality
- Ajñāna as the collective cause of the world

The modern era: Predominant in this period were the teachings of Swami Vivekananda and Sri Ramakrishna. The changes these gurus made adapted Advaita to the present world's needs and the day-to-day challenges of life. While Swami Vivekananda reconciled Advaita to modern science by stating that the philosophy of Advaita was not just a belief but the science of consciousness, Sri Ramakrishna popularized śivajñāne jīva-sevā – The gospel of service to man being equal to service to God.

Advaita Vedānta: The Planes of Existence

In classical Advaita Vedānta, there are three planes of existence:

• Prātibhāsika; Sanskrit प्रातिभासिक: This is the plane that deals with illusions, or illusions masking themselves as reality.

• Vyāvahārika Satta; Sanskrit व्यवहारिक: This is the plane that deals with the worldly reality that can be empirically proven.

• Pāramārthika Satta; Sanskrit: पारमार्थिक: This is the plane of absolute, true reality or existence.

Viśiṣṭādvaita, Also Known as Qualified Non-Dualism (Sanskrit: विशिष्टाद्वैत)

This advocates Monism. One of the major proponents of this school of thought was Ramanuja, although the movement began with Vaishnava or devotion to Lord Vishnu in South India in the 7th century.

The monist movement started in the 10th century with Nathamuni, a brahman or priest of the Srirangam temple in Tamil Nadu. Yamuna succeeded Nathamuni in the 11th century, and Yamuna handed over to Ramanuja (1017- 1137).

Ramanuja was a priest at the Varadharāja Perumal temple, Kānchipuram, in Tamil Nadu. He wrote the Sri Bhāshya – a commentary on the Brahma sutras – among other works and believed that his philosophy was consistent with the Advaita Vedanta only with one minor difference.

According to Sri Ramanuja, the only way to become one with the divine is devotion (Bhakti). Man is a spark or ray of the divine, and mokṣa or release is not dependent on a series of rebirths or reincarnation but on complete devotion to the almighty who mercifully aids the devotee in attaining freedom. In qualified non-dualism, brahman is the ultimate reality that humans strive to become. Just like our souls are one with the body, God is one with the world. This ideology is the reason monism is called Viśiṣṭādvaita or Advaita with some uniqueness.

These principles are the cornerstones of Viśiṣṭādvaita:

- **Hitā (Sanskrit हिता):** This is self-realization achieved through the surrender of self or Prapatti, and complete devotion or Bhakti.

- **Tattvá (Sanskrit तत्त्व):** This refers to reality, the essence of life, and real truth. This is knowledge of the three primary entities: Ajiva (the non-sentient entity), Jiva (sentient beings or living things), and Īśvara (the supreme being, ruler of all manifestations, and the inherent giver of grace and mercy based on karma).

- **Puruṣārtha (Sanskrit पुरुषार्थ):** The object of pursuit or the goal to be attained, which in this case is liberation or mokṣa.

Chapter Three: Sadhana and Samadhi Explained

Abhyāsa And Vairāgya: Spiritual Practices for Sadhana

Abhyāsa and Vairāgya are two crucial concepts in the yoga sutras of Patañjali. Yoga Sutra chapter 1, verse 12 says, "Abhyāsa-Vairāgyābhyam tan-nirodhah," which translates to "Practice and detachment are the means to still the movements of consciousness." (Light on the Yoga Sutras of Patanjali by B.K.S. Iyengar). Consciousness, in this case, is known as Chitta.

Abhyāsa is a combination of two Sanskrit words: Abhi, meaning "greatly" or "over," and Aayyas, meaning action, effort, or practice. Abhyāsa refers to spiritual practice, beliefs, or rituals continuously practiced over a period to achieve and maintain mental, physical, and spiritual tranquility. Amritabindu Upanishad speaks of the immeasurable power of the human mind, saying "Man eva manushyanam karanam bandh mokshayoh," which means "Mind is the cause of renunciation and bondages."

In the Bhagavad-Gītā, abhyāsa is mentioned by Lord Krishna as an essential means of controlling desire and the mind. Abhyāsa implies mindfulness in every action and serves as a reminder we remain passionate and present in all things we do because, in the end, vigilant enterprise pays off. Yoga is a path of delight, not despair. Thus, cultivating enthusiasm ensures that our interest does not wane with prolonged effort, as no one can approach mokṣa without joy.

Vairāgya (वैराग्य) is an abstract noun derived from the word virāga (joining vi, which means "without" and rāga, which means "passion, feeling, emotion, interest"). Vairāgya could be said to mean dispassion or an ascetic stance on life. Hindu philosophers and yoga masters who were advocates of vairāgya teach that neutrality, especially towards pleasures and pain are the only way to achieve mokṣa. For this reason, vairāgya is more a state of mind than it is a practice.

Vairāgya does not imply repulsion towards material things or suppressing your desire for them. It only advocates balance, using Vivek (discernment or spiritual judgment) to strive for fulfillment between one's inner spiritual life and their external or physical needs so undue attachments dissolve naturally.

For this to happen, the student or devotee must see all entries as expressions of the brahman (superior cosmic consciousness). Once we understand that everything in life is temporary, it becomes easier to let go at the proper time because freedom from desire or vitṛṣṇatva helps achieve vasīkāra or total control.

Abhyāsa and Vairāgya are the two pillars of yoga sadhana and resemble two sides of a coin, with abhyāsa denoting persistence and vairāgya disinterest. They are both essential in gaining mastery of the mind because while abhyāsa drives a devotee toward peace and perfection, vairāgya helps one remain tranquil, unfettered by materialism to balance the efforts brought on by persistence.

Yoga tries to create the conditions of Abhyāsa and Vairāgya to control our vritti and create new samskaras, slowly but controlling desire by refusing attachments, be it in the form of possessions, thoughts, or feelings. To yogis, attachments breed sorrow. Abhyāsa and Vairāgya are neither positive nor negative. It is all a matter of perception. Just like when an object is too close to the eye, it becomes somewhat invisible, but such an item becomes clear when held at a distance.

Abhyāsa puts in the effort while vairagya adjusts our attitudes to perform our duties well and without fear. Without the control supplied by vairāgya, our efforts will lead to varied interests, which are difficult to control. Abhyāsa without vairagya leads us to begin a task full-throttle and abandon it halfway because we can't seem to stop our minds from wandering or worrying.

The principles of Abhyāsa and Vairāgya are applied to everything in life, including lifestyle disorders such as addiction, depression, obesity, insomnia, etc. There are so many ways yoga positively affects health. Yoga nidras, asanas, and pranayama are common in abhyāsa. Niṣkāmakarma (selflessness) and Dhyana (meditation) help us maintain physical fitness, handle daily stressors, and improve the quality of life.

Levels of Sadhana

The four levels of sadhana in terms of abhyāsa and vairāgya include:

1. Mrdu (Mild)

- Abhyāsa: Painstaking, indefinite practice

- Vairāgya: Yatamāna separating sense from action leading to Ārambhāvasthā or commencement.

2. Madhya (Moderate)

- Abhyāsa: Discipline and methodical practice

- Vairagya: Vyatireka (avoiding desire) leading to Ghatavasthā or understanding the inner workings of the body.

3. Adhimātra (Intense)

- Abhyāsa: Scientific decisive practice

- Vairagya: Ekendriya — Quieting the mind, leading to Paricayāvasthā or personal knowledge of mind and self.

4. Tivra Samvegin Adhimātrataman (Very Intense)

- Abhyāsa: Purity and religious devotion

- Vairagya: Vasīkāra (overcoming all desire) leading to Nispattyā or Paravairāgya (extreme detachment) where one transcends mortality to perceive the soul.

The Place of Consciousness in Samādhi

The word Citta or Chitta (Sanskrit चित्त) comes from the root word "Cit" meaning to observe or to perceive. Loosely translated, citta represents the mind in all its forms: unconscious, semi-conscious, and conscious. Citta is not equal to puruṣa, nor is it separate from Prakriti. It is the bridge to understanding the synergy between Prakriti (the seen) and puruṣa (the seer).

In yoga sutra 2.23 it states, "स्वस्वामिशक्त्योः स्वरूपोपलब्धिहेतुः संयोगः ॥२३॥-. Satchidananda explains this, saying, "The union of Owner (Puruṣa) and owned (Prakṛiti) causes the recognition of the nature and powers of them both." Regardless of the omnipresence of Prakriti and puruṣa, the all-pervading citta is held back by the ego.

The Functions of the Citta

The three primary functions of the citta include buddhi, manas, and ahamkara. These functions do not frequently appear in the yoga sutras but are commonly seen in Sānkhya philosophy that shares guiding principles with Sri Patañjali's yoga sutras.

Buddhi is the purest, most subtle form following the evolution of Prakriti. It is the middle man between spirit (puruṣa) and nature (Prakriti). Ahamkara, the three gunas (forces of nature), the senses, and the elements all evolve from buddhi. Buddhi is the discerning faculty of the mind. It takes on impressions from manas. After comparing and contrasting these impressions, citta in buddhi uses judgment to categorize and store them for retrieval.

Manas is the memory or recording faculty of the citta. It is the entry point of all impressions and is deeply involved in the function of the senses.

Ahamkara is the part of the mind known as the ego. Ahamkara claims the impressions stored in the mamas and buddhi as its own and serves as the seat of individuality. It is at the level of ahamkara that suffering or dukkha is born. The ego prevents one from identifying with puruṣa. Expectations such as desire, craving, anger, and compassion are all feelings familiar to ahamkara. The first task for any yogi is to eliminate the selfish feelings pervading ahamkara.

Samadhi or enlightenment is only attained after ego transcends, and the mind recognizes oneness with puruṣa. This is because samadhi is more than gaining above rational wisdom. It is a state that exceeds the shackles of the mind, the ego, personal bias, the physical senses, and the limitations of human thought processes. Samadhi is a journey that begins with holding on to the attention brought about by the object used in meditation — the perceivable form of Prakriti.

Kinds of Samadhi

Samprajñāta-Samādhi (Sanskrit: सविकल्पसमाधि)

This is the samadhi in which samskaras escape destruction. For this reason, it is often called Savikalpa samadhi or Sabija Samadhi (samadhi with support) because the seeds of samskara remain. This form of samadhi requires conscious or concrete meditation in which the yogi is fully aware of the world, themselves, and inner peace. This samadhi is dualistic in thought as there is a distinction between the object and the observer.

Vyasa's commentary proposes the four levels (bhumi) of Samprajñāta from the surface to the deepest level. The first level is **Savitarka Samādhi.** This is also known as deliberative meditation or Vitarka (वितर्क) and is defined as the awareness or consciousness of particulars; it involves contemplating the world in space and time. In this level, the yogi meditates while being conscious of a physical object, such as the statue of a deity (murti), the flame of a lamp, etc. This meditation is possible because perception is easy. The object is familiar and relatable to our senses. When this meditation ends, it becomes Nirvitarka-samāpatti.

The second level is **Savichara Samadhi.** There is a loss of time and space. It has the citta focused on an object not easily perceived by the human senses. This level is designated by the clarity of the inner mind (Visaradya). Instead, these archetypes are believed to exist based on inference through the cognition of the sense organs. Examples of these subtle objects (archetypes) are; prana (inner breath), Buddhi (intellect), and chakra (energy centers). This meditation ends in Nirvichara-samāpatti. Yoga Sutra 1.48 refers to this state as Rtambhara, intellectual essence, or truthful wisdom.

At the third level, you have **Sananda Samadhi.** This is the level of conscious bliss, activated when the yogi has increased Sattva Guna (force of equilibrium, purity, and harmony). Citta has progressed beyond the objective world, beyond reflection, intellect, and reasoning to settle into the sattvic (pure) joyous mind. This is the reason this level of samadhi is called "Blissful samadhi."

The fourth level is **Asmita Samadhi.** Here, the bliss has evaporated with consciousness penetrating all the way to Buddhi. At this stage, Buddhi has left behind all traces of the material world to be in tune with puruṣa. Puruṣa then becomes the object of meditation, and all that is left behind is pure sattvic ego. At this stage, one gains awareness of their individuality to embrace the state "I Am" in its most accurate elemental form.

The yogi gets exposed to the divinity within themselves. You must exercise caution at this level, as the ego is a double-edged sword. When used with a clean heart, it can foster progress and help humanity, but spiritual progress can become stunted with greed.

Yogi practicing Samprajnata must do it with a selfless and pure heart to avoid the yogi from abusing their abilities.

Asamprajñāta Samādhi (Sanskrit: असम्प्रज्ञातसमाधि)

This is also called Nirvikalpa Samadhi or Nirbija Samadhi ("samadhi without seed). This stage of samādhi represents the highest state of samādhi. It is a state of bliss obtained where the yogi has discovered the highest self. Synonymous with enlightenment, this stage makes the mind a blank slate where the devotee is free from all material thought. Citta ensures the yogi sees unity and perfection in everything.

Asamprajñāta allows the yogi's consciousness (astral, causal, and physical) to reach a state of perfect non-duality where no differences exists between the universe and self. This form of samadhi brings independence (kaivalya) and excellent awareness about the deliberate practice of the cessation of mental impressions or modifications.

Samprajñāta Samādhi differs from Asamprajñāta Samādhi because the former requires support or ālambanas. In Samprajñāta or cognitive samādhi, the citta needs an object to focus on, be it subtle or gross, until dharma-megha (the perfect super-consciousness) is attained.

The Hazards of Samādhi

Samādhi can provide benefits and risks to the practitioner. Meditation (samādhi) brings calm and peace. What danger could exist with peace, one may ask? That once the mind is in a state of calm, it is possible to get lost in bliss so that citta refuses to return to reality.

This question is the reason for Upacara samādhi. Upacara samādhi tethers us to reality so that even while in samādhi jhana, the mind can leave a state of deep, sustained calm to comprehend reality. Refusal to do this sharpens the mind to a point like a new butcher's knife one refuses to use. Wisdom from samādhi becomes an enemy because of the lack of awareness. There is no comprehension or clarity with all that knowledge.

Chapter Four: Savitarka Versus Nirvitarka Samadhi

Understanding the Serenity Called Samādhi

Buddha once said to Bodhisattva Bhadrapāla, "There is a single dharma practice one should rehearse and preserve. One should cultivate these before following any other dharmas, one which is most praiseworthy and foremost among all qualities: The quality of meditation where all buddha of the present stand before one."

Centering the mind is like building a home for oneself. Khaṇika Samādhi is a temporary concentration akin to an unroofed house without thatch. Upacara samādhi is a threshold concentration identical to a roofed and tiled home. After upacara samādhi is fixed contemplation called Appanā samādhi, a type of meditation resembling a sturdy house built from bricks. Training the mind to be centered is like gaining refuge. A centered mind is like a weapon, a fortress that keeps one safe from the flood of worldly pain and suffering.

When the mind is centered and free from hindrances, the body feels well. This state where the mind and body are both strong is called Samādhi Balam – The strength of focus. Focused concentration leaves room for discernment, the ability to see and handle stress. As mentioned earlier, the state of samādhi or trance is two-fold: Samprajñāta and Asamprajñāta. The former has man's consciousness closed off from external disturbances but leaves internal or initiated activities to continue undisturbed. The latter has all these qualities in cessation.

It is essential to know there are entities naturally existing in a state of samādhi. These beings are known as Prakriti-layas and Videhas and possess a cosmic consciousness, hence they need not attain samadhi by exertion. A Videha is a deva (Sanskrit: देव or celestial being) who has lost bodily awareness. Videha's understanding of self is not limited to their body.

The Prakriti-laya's sense of self-awareness is one with the universe. For these beings, they feel merged with the universe. The videhas and Prakriti-layas are Mukta (liberated) from the very start. You may find them in whatever world cycle is ongoing, in future Kalpa (कल्प), which is the time between the creation and recreation of All That Is or the cosmos.

For ordinary entities like us humans, the requirements for liberation have been written in the sutras thus: **"श्रद्धावीमस्मय णृ तसभाणधप्र⬜न्नवू कय इतयषे** -śraddhā-vīrya-smṛti samādhi-prajñā-pūrvaka itareṣām."** Translated, it means, "To others (this Samadhi) comes through faith, energy, memory, concentration, and discrimination of the real." In simpler terms, for humans to obtain samādhi, they must learn to suppress citta. Suppressing citta requires enormous stores of energy, meditation, faith, wisdom, and a retentive memory.

All these qualities may be desirable to become a successful yogi. However, one should be made aware that the level of success heavily depends on the time and effort put into the practice. The quickest and safest way to obtain samadhi is through the love of God. Loving God with the heart and soul ceases all mental functions. Suspension of these functions is necessary as Īśvara is omniscient, the mentor of all.

In the sutras, Īśvara's is a distinct Puruṣa, untouched by the vehicles of affliction, action, and fruition. Īśvara's mystic name is **OM, or AUM** (written with the generic Devanagari symbol ॐ). Om is a simple sound with a powerful meaning. OM is the entire world compressed into one syllable that signifies the unity of heart, body, and soul. Om is at the heart of yoga and represents the essence of atman and ultimate reality.

OM is everywhere. It is in the rush of the tornado's winds, the crackle of a flame or the rumble in the ocean's belly. The primordial sound OM exists in the drama of creation and deep meditation after stilling the mind chatter.

Reciting the mystical sound OM consistently while meditating on the letters allows the atman (inner self) to manifest. Distractions will abound, but once a devotee fixes their attention on God – the one point and truth – then they will achieve samādhi. Samādhi is not only experienced by closeted monks or celibate yogis trapped in Tibetan monasteries or Indian caves. There are great yogi and yogini who are parents running a typical household. This goes to show that enlightenment is only difficult, not impossible.

The Way to Attain Samadhi

Sage Patañjali gave clear instructions to help us all attain enlightenment or Samādhi (Sanskrit समाधी, also called samāpatti). According to the commentary offered by Vyasa on the samadhi pada (first sutra), the thinking mind, or mind-stuff, or citta, has five states:

- Mūḍha: The torpid or lethargic state
- Ekagra: The focused state
- Ksipta: The restless state
- Nirrudha: The restricted state
- Viksipta: The distracted state

The only states considered as yoga are the ekagra state and the nirrudha state. It is the subliminal impressions (samskaras) and distractions (vikshepas) we hold in mind, which cause the mental fluctuations or chitta we must contend with. According to Patañjali, there are nine major classifications of distraction which we must deal with:

- Lethargy or Styana
- Sickness or Vyadhi
- Doubt or Samsaya
- Worldliness or Avirati
- Wavering in concentration, or Anavas thitatva
- Listlessness or Alasya
- Carelessness or Pramada
- Failing to concentrate, or Alabdhabhumikatva
- Errors in perceptions or Bhrantidarshana

When you're in a state of meditative consciousness or in trance, you're in Samadhi. The etymology of Samadhi is based on Sam-a-dha, meaning "to bring together." This is the word used to denote a mind unified, or Ekaggata. Samadhi persist when both spirit and intellect are in unity (Brahman). It happens when you are conscious of the ego, anger, fear, joy, or any other emotion, and yet can remain focused on simply being. The condition for obtaining the power of samadhi lies in securing release from samsara, or the cycle of death and rebirth.

Levels of Samadhi

Level One: Savikalpa Samadhi. This stage happens when you surpass all mental activity. According to Patañjali, you enter into another world and remain undisturbed by the fickle concept of space and time for a short period. You see the cycle of things. This level has four stages; Savitarka, Savichara, Sa-Anada, and Sa-Asmita.

Level Two: Nirvikalpa Samadhi. In this state of samadhi, samskara and the ego have ceased, and only pure consciousness is left. The heart is fully awake and feels larger than life itself. It feels like living life at 200%, where one possesses infinite power and bliss that helps you see the divinity in everything. This stage can last from a few hours to a few days. Because of the endless joy in this state, many who reach here do not wish to return. However, there is a caveat: Anyone who stays in nirvikalpa samadhi for over 21 days will have their soul depart from their physical body for good.

Level Three: Sahaja Samadhi. This stage of natural or spontaneous enlightenment. This stage is where the yogi can maintain inner silence in their day to day lives. This way, the yogi experiences and holds nirvikalpa radiating and manifesting light every second. Here, one experiences unified consciousness to become one filled with divine grace.

Level Four: Dharma Megha Samadhi. Also known as the cloud of virtue. This stage arises when one has lost the desire for enlightenment. This stage is not gained through personal effort. But it is a divine gift that reveals itself when actions come to nothing. At this stage of samadhi, karmic bondages melt away so the yogi may will anything into being by the power of intention.

The Ten Types of Samādhi

All types of samādhi involve the complete absorption of the yogi in an intense state of mind concentration. The only difference between each state is the different levels of consciousness.

- **Savitarka samādhi (सवितर्क):** This is also called Vitarka samprajñāta samādhi. It is the initial stage of Dhyana (contemplation, abstract reflection) and the first form of samādhi. As the yogi or yogini practices consistently at this stage, he or she breaks through pratyāya (mind content or ideas) to reach vitarka.

- **Nirvitarka samādhi (निर्वितर्क):** Vitarka comes from a Sanskrit word वितर्क. Its roots are वि (Vi) and तर्क (Tarka). Vitarka means inquiry or reasoning. Vitarka goes hand in hand with samādhi as it is the nature of the mind to inquire about the object of meditation continuously.

In nirvitarka samadhi, the questioning mind is powered by one who has achieved union with the object of meditation. Nirvitarka involves creatively examining the object upon which you are mediating until you perceive deeper and subtler dimensions you would never ordinarily notice about it. This examination takes you so deep you discover tanmatras (Sanskrit: तन्मात्र), which are subtle elements such as taste, smell, sound, touch, form.

The knowledge from vitarka samadhi terminates at the level of tanmatras. For the yogi to see through to the composites of subtle elements, the mind needs more focusing, hence vicāra. Nirvitarka samadhi resembles a vacuum. Breaking through pratyāya to release artha (meaning) allows consciousness to move from the outward direction (paranga cetane) inwards (pratyak cetana). This boundary is Asamprajñāta samadhi at vitarka to the vicāra border.

- **Nirvicāra samādhi (निर्विचार):** Vicār (विचार) in Sanskrit means deliberation. Its roots are the Sanskrit symbols वि- (vi) and चर् (cara), meaning "to roam, move or have knowledge of." Vicāra is a yoga practice in Vedanta philosophy that also accompanies samadhi. Vicāra is a clarified form of inquiry compared to vitarka and is attuned to discovering the tanmatras. The mind during nirvicāra samādhi develops a resonance with the object of meditation. In yoga sutra 1.44, Sri Patañjali teaches "एतयैव सविचारा निर्विचारा च सूक्ष्मविषया व्याख्याता ॥४४॥" or "Etayaiva savicārā nirvicārā cha sūksma-visaya vyākhyātā," which when translated means, "By this, deliberative and non-deliberative thoughts concerning subtle things are explained."

Nirvicārā is the dissolution of pratyāya at the vicāra level. Once pratyak cetane is reached, this is called nirvicāra, and from there, one transcends to Ananda. In sutra 1.47, Patañjali teaches "निर्विचारवैशारद्येऽध्यात्मप्रसादः ॥४७॥- " or "Nirvicāra-vaiśāradye- 'dhyātma-prasādah." This verse means that the constant flow of nirvicārā samādhi results in the pervasiveness of coherence of atman (eternal self.)

- **Ānanda (आनन्द),** meaning bliss or joy. This is the aspect of samādhi beyond subtle elements. Ananda is the joyful mind free from stress, burden, or fear. Incredibly satisfying, this state of samādhi is more than our typical experience of happiness. Ananda reflects unbounded bliss that is self. This form of pleasure may make us believe that we have attained enlightenment, tempting us to halt our self-realization efforts.

- **Asmitā (अस्मिता).** "Asmi" loosely translates to "Am." In first-person, asmi means "I Am." The suffix "ta" means "ness." At this stage, the yogi has reached the highest possible stage of "I Am-ness," the most profound degree of consciousness and the highest degree of vritti. Pratyāya disintegrates when Asamprajñāta is accomplished at Asmita. The yogi experiences nothing except pure, blank consciousness. This occurrence leads to the next samādhi known as Nirbīja samādhi.

- **Nirbīja Samādhi (निर्बीजसमाधि):** Aphorisms concerning this state are abstract and challenging to comprehend. One can deduct from the sutra that at this level, the yogi comes to terms with emptiness existing between moments in time.

- **Dharma Megha samādhi (धर्ममेघसमाधि):** This samadhi is the non-dual embodiment of kaivalya-freedom, absolute one-ness). This is the highest samādhi obtained at the moment of biological death. In classic Hindu literature, this samādhi is described as "a state where the mind progressively abandons the concept of both meditator and meditation." The effect of this samadhi is the cessation and conversion of all Karma stored up over immeasurable lives and the "evolution of pure Dharma (धर्म) virtue, law, way of righteousness."

The Difference Between Sabija and Nirbija Samādhi

Patanjali divided samādhi into two main types; Sabija and Nirbija. Sabija samādhi is also called samādhi with seeds or lower samādhi and has nine sutras dedicated to its understanding in the sutras of

Patañjali (sutras 1.42- 50). In contrast, Nirbīja samādhi (without seeds) has only one sutra that explains the apex of all samādhi.

Sabija Samādhi

The emphasis Patañjali places on sabija is a warning about the many ways things could go wrong once one becomes careless meditating at any point in sabija samādhi. Sabija requires commitment and vigilance in immersing the mind with purity. Purity here is developed by practicing selflessness, compassion and dispassion, and kindness.

Sabija also involves mind discipline and finding a balance between yogi meditation and day to day living. Mental stupor and inertia are hard to avoid or detect during sabija samādhi, which is why in the sutra, Patañjali urges us to rid our minds of tamas (burden, inertia) and fill it with sattva (purity, light). Sabija samādhi is associated with prajñā (intuition, wisdom).

As one practices meditation, the mind sharpens so it becomes easier to distinguish good from evil and final decisions are doubt-free. There will no longer be a fear of the unknown as you walk on the path of attaining self-mastery. In sutra 1.48, it states, "ऋतम्भरा तत्र प्रज्ञा ॥४८॥- Rtambharaa tatra praj~jaa." In this sutra, Patañjali explains how intuitive wisdom in Rtam (eternal laws and cosmic order) resides in sabija samādhi so that the illuminative insight from rtam helps one see the seeds (bija) of samskara (impressions of past actions) or karmic deeds.

Samskaras can be painful or delightful. The discerning mind in sabija picks up which seeds are nurtured, and which should be discarded. Vairāgya enhances this stage. Sabija samādhi is the most dynamic stage of the journey to enlightenment.

The mind's potentials are awakened, single-pointed, and filled with rtam, so it discovers it has been gifted a body to serve the soul and knows to what extent human desires should be fulfilled, disciplined, or withheld. This revelation of higher truth is the distinctive trait of sabija samādhi.

Nirbija Samādhi

The yogi in nirbīja has no seeds of meditation. He is the sole object of their search. The yogi's realm of nirbīja is achieved with the ability to see all objects in the realm of prakṛiti, including themselves, as they are. The difference between sabīja and nirbīja is that the former requires the presence of an item (seed) whose reality must be realized.

The seeds exist in prakṛiti and are the focus of meditation (samayama). Bija can be anything from a rock or a flame to a thought or an experience. Nirbija samadhi, on the other hand, is the proverbial eye of the needle. Extremely difficult yet possible to attain, it is the realm of the subtle and the objectless objective. While sabija samādhi has a yogi seeking himself while a veil blurs his vision, nirbīja is spiritual evolution that tears off the veil to achieve enlightenment.

In nirbīja lies spiritual bliss, spontaneous enlightenment, and liberation from thoughts, conditioning, and attachments. Nirbīja is why in present-day yoga, this samadhi is synonymous with the awakening of the kundalini. It is essential to understand that nirbīja is not the result of constant practice but occurs with the sudden surrender of both practice and practitioner depending on the practice's direction.

Nirbija is the natural evolution from sabija that occurs when atman has lost its power. The total surrender of karmic impressions leaves nirbīja behind to reveal the last state called dharma-megha samādhi.

Chapter Five: The Philosophy of Sādhanā and Its Connection to Kleśa

Sādhanā (साधना) is a spiritual practice and a lifelong commitment done to release us from the thorns of human limitation in a bid to increase our connection with the supreme. Sadhana is not for the merely curious individuals on the search for siddhi (psychic powers). It is for people dedicated to the incredible voyage that is salvation.

Sādhanā is attained by studying religious scripture, prayer, association with the enlightened, and meditation.

These are all necessary practices because the path of spirituality has its thorns and slippery slopes. With a firm resolve, training, and patience, the end product of sadhana is a better outlook on life, joy, and communication with God. A sādhaka, sādhak, or sādhaj (Sanskrit: साधक) is a person dedicated to following a specific sādhanā designed to realize an ultimate goal.

A true sādhaka is one who can differentiate between what serves his spiritual purpose and what keeps him attached to the world, preventing him from expanding his consciousness. All the mental exercises of sadhana are done to rid us of Kleśa (afflictions or mental blocks) that hold us back from wholeness and God-realization.

According to yoga, sutra 2.2 "सभाणधबावनाथ्य शतनकू यिाथिय ॥ २ ॥-samādhibhāvanārthaḥ kleśatanūkaraṇārthaśca," which translates to "The intent is to gradually attain contemplation (samadhi) and diminish the causes of suffering (kleśas).

Kleśa: The Root of Human Suffering

Kleśa (Sanskrit क्लेश, also klesha) are mental obstacles or afflictions that become a den for samskaras, which develop into actions and accompanying karma. One of the philosophies in Vedanta reminds us that when enlightenment is absent, life contains suffering. Suffering is not to be confused with pain. Pain is discomfort, mental, physical, or emotional, that happens to us while suffering is how we interpret, identify, and react to pain.

The third śloka of the second chapter of Patañjali's Yoga sūtra mentions five afflictions or poisons (Sanskrit: pañcakleśā). "These five afflictions are ávidyā (ignorance or misapprehension concerning reality), asmitā (egoism), raga (attachment), dveṣa (hate or aversion), and abhiniveśāḥ (fear of death from clinging ignorantly to life and the present).

Ávidyā or Ignorance: This happens when you forget or are unaware of the true nature of reality. In Ávidyā, you are in the dark about your true nature as a spiritual being, pure boundless awareness, immortal consciousness, and eternal timelessness that was never born and will never perish. Unfortunately, the hustle and bustle of everyday living have hidden truth from our conscious awareness.

This kleśa makes us see the impure as pure, temporal as permanent, and painful as pleasant. Avidya is commonly translated as ignorance but is better described as misinterpretation or misapprehension. This distinction is because ignorance bellies a total lack of understanding, while misinterpretation represents an inaccuracy in interpretation, leading to comprehension errors.

In Patanjali's yoga sutras, Āvidyā is considered the breeding ground for the other four kleśas, be they feeble, intercepted, dormant, or sustained. Simply put, dukkha (suffering) are modifications of qualitative and quantitative expressions of Āvidyā.

Feeble Kleśa implies that mild suffering is experienced. The tentacles of sadhana weaken this form of Kleśa. An example of sadhana includes the practice of yoga to transcend the ego. Intercepted Kleśa are those constantly oscillating, but the yogi puts in work to control them. Dormant kleśa are latent afflictions. They exist but have not yet found an avenue favorable for their expression. Sustained Kleśa is those kleśa in full bloom, unhindered, and expressed. Not that we cannot have goals or desires. We all wish for either, beauty, fame, wealth, or mundane things the media portray as paths to happiness.

Yoga and meditation teach us that everything in nature is temporary, changing as time passes. The only unchanging reality is purusa, which is the universal principle and pure consciousness we are all a part of. Purusa is unaffected and unlimited by gross and subtle elements.

Purusa never evolves. So, the pleasure we get from deifying ideals that frequently change is not purusa. These ideals can be anything from the need to fit in with a particular crowd for praise or the temporary pleasure from the indulgence of food and sugar-laden snacks.

The Seven States of Ávidyā

- Disbelief that union with the soul as taught in yoga is impossible and acting as though it is so.

- Unsteadiness or a fickle mind

- Existing with the association of pain

- Creating conditions that make you undergo sorrow

- Inferiority and a mean disposition

- Accepting or mistaking the perishable body for atman.

- Living with affliction, agony, and misery.

A telltale sign that avidya no longer has a hold on us is when our constant identification with attachments, possessions, and position wavers and diminishes. A light bulb goes off in our heads so we realize we are not better off with them, and we will not suffer without them.

Asmitā or Egoism or a False Sense of Self: This Kleśa is the firstborn of Ávidyā and a case of mistaken identity. Asmitā is the culprit that leads one to confuse the seer (atman) with instruments of seeing (manas or mind, citta or mind-stuff, indriyāṇi or sense organs, and buddhi or determinative faculty). You live in a house, but you're not made from bricks or mortar now, are you? Asmita is similar to the metaphorical bhishma in the Bhagavad Gita.

The ego manifests itself differently. Ego touches on everything from the clothes we wear, the food we eat, and even where we live. How would you introduce yourself if you are asked the question, "Who are you?" You would likely start with your name, age, profession, and maybe marital status. You might throw in a hobby you excel at for the proverbial "icing on the cake." This is all-natural behavior because asmita results from the natural human tendency to over-identify ourselves with thoughts and feelings.

Say you are a doctor by profession. What happens when you can't practice medicine anymore? Will you subject yourself to pain because of the number of years you have invested time and effort in medical school? Ego is the reflection of purusa on citta. They may both look like, but purusa is the real deal, while asmita is a cheap duplicate.

Once we let those feelings about ourselves go, we would never suffer hurt, worry, or insult, jumping head-first onto the emotional bandwagon that is the current backdrop nowadays.

Yoga teaches us not to see things as they are but as we are. One solution to asmita is expanding our sense of self to include others. This allows a sense of shared consciousness so we feel the link between our soul and others. This is called connecting with the "all" instead of with the "particular." Asmita is often confused with ahamkara. Ahamkara is the force or power that creates individuality. Because of ahamkara, we can confidently say," I am a woman," or "I am a man."

Rāga or Attachment: Sutra II:7 states, "Raga is the attachment or inclination that dwells on pleasure." Raga is the attraction to and pursuing pleasures that please the senses.

The chain of events that lead to raga can happen suddenly or by accident. We buy an object that makes us happy or partake in an activity that pleases us. The temporary high from that pleasure leads us to spend time, resources, and energy to repeat that experience or stay on that pleasurable wavelength. With time, this desire forces us to act mindlessly, and when we don't get what we want, we feel sad.

When we get what we want, we want even more. Rage then becomes an affliction trapping us in a vicious cycle of desire where we continuously seek things or people that make us happy.

Even yoga students can get attached to specific asanas or exercises. Spiritual growth forces us to take on challenges, shake things up a little bit, yet staying detached from the outcome. Accepting the impermanence of life and embracing each passing moment is how to remove the raga's veil.

Dveṣa or Aversion: After the colorings of asmita and avidya are added to apparent manifestations; our sensory impressions could interpret the "reality" so that ahamkara colors it with dvesa or dislike, adding another false identity to "I" based on aversion.

Say you see a painting, and you decide that colors on the canvas do not appeal to you, so the picture is ugly. This dislike or bias is an example of dvesa. Impressions and false identities get stored in the citta like coins in a piggy bank waiting to pop up when the occasion arises.

With dvesa, you avoid anything that is unpleasant or threatens your ego. dvesa is one of the most common causes of addiction or self-harm. You drink to escape your problems. You become a glutton to eat your worries away or avoid uncomfortable situations. Dvesa causes affliction by forcing the mind to build walls of fear and negativity instead of facing issues head-on.

Conquering dvesa will involve disapproval with vairagya so your aversion is not clouded by avidya or bias but in complete awareness of your state of being and the power of discernment that comes with buddhi. This is the only way dvesa does not form a samskara. The true self knows nothing belongs to them, and nothing is a part of them.

Abhiniveśāḥ or Fear of the Unknown: This is the fifth and final Kleśa. This fear could be a part of raga or dvesa. Attraction and aversion are afflictions that force us to live like we fear dying. This kleśa is not easily battled as most people refuse to acknowledge their existence in their subconscious mind.

Every desire has a layer of abhiniveśāḥ to protect the desire from losing its appeal or presence. Our fear forces our bodies to react in a myriad of ways: Nail-biting, fidgeting, sweaty palms and forehead, muscle spasms, etc., which tells you something is going on in your mind's deepest recesses, no matter how you try to deny it.

Combating Kleśa

Because they are all seeds of avidya, kleśa is an obstacle to self-realization, binding us to the continuous cycle of death and rebirth because of samskaras. To combat these mental afflictions in our consciousness, one needs to reflect on how they influence our behavior and thought process.

Reflection is the only way to achieve self-awareness. The next step is to awaken our inner wisdom using deep meditation to embrace our true selves. The last and final step is to seek knowledge, find our purpose while recognizing the objectives that do not serve us, still the mind, and set new intentions to manifest the change we desire.

The Guṇa and Their Place in Yogic Belief

In yoga, the world is divided into two categories: Prakriti or illusion and purusa or reality. Everything you can find in maya or prakriti has three very important qualities or guna (Sanskrit गु, meaning quality, or strand, or fiber). Guna is present everywhere and in all objects to varying degrees, some dominant, others not so much. The three gunas are:

- Rajas (activity, passion, desire, sorrow, emotion)
- Tamas (destruction, darkness, lethargy, inertia)
- Sattva (purity, harmony, happiness, or knowledge)

The Influence of the Guna and Finding Balance

We can consciously alter the degrees of the dominance of guna in our bodies and minds. Depending on which guna dominates at a time, our perception, mood, and attachments may be affected. For instance, when we are sattvic, we feel happy, harmonious, and calm with a glass half full disposition. A rajasic state implies hyperactivity and determination to perform tasks, while a lack of motivation characterizes a tamasic state, so our moods become cynical and sour. These three qualities are needed in life, none more than the other. Rajas help us get up every morning. Tamas reminds us to rest, and sattva helps us with mindfulness, self-awareness, and clarity.

Yoga does not exist to keep us purely in sattva. Stay sattvic long enough, and tamas eventually follow. Embracing the change is the balance you need after all; no one is always chipper, peaceful, or unmotivated. Even a broken clock tells the time right twice daily. There cannot be sattva without rajas and tamas; embracing our constantly changing gunas is not where mastery ends. The goal is detachment from the three gunas to see the reality beyond the illusion. This way, you are indifferent to pleasure or pain, sorrow, or joy.

Karmāśaya and the Fruits of Karma

Karmāśaya (कर्माशय) is also known as the sea of karma or receptacle of works. It is derived from karma कर्म, meaning "action, works" and āśaya आशय. This receptacle stores up the effects of actions from a previous lifetime recurring as new impulses to action. Karmasaya remains until all its root causes are gotten rid of. These roots are the fruits of karma.

Karmasaya in Hindu literature is used to explain desire (vāsanā) and saṃskāra.

The total of accumulated karma is known as sañcita karma. In Swami Sivananda's teachings, when the physical body dies, we carry our astral body of 17 elements (tattvas) and karmasaya to the mental plane.

Karmasaya is rooted in the Kleśas and experienced in the lives both seen, and unseen as written in sutra 2.12: "Karmāśaya or latent impression of action based on afflictions, becomes active in this life or in a life to come."

Karma, Reincarnation, and Mokṣa

Reincarnation is a concept existing in various cultures and religions. In Buddhist literature, there are two occurrences tied to reincarnation: Karma and moksa. Hinduism believes that our deeds (karma) determine the quality of our lives. If you live a good life, you stack up good karma and vice versa. Karma can be produced in four ways:

- Thoughts
- Personal actions
- Words
- Actions others do under our instruction.

These actions (good or bad) create karmic fruits carried in a receptacle (karmasaya) into the next life through atman. Reincarnation is the rebirth of an individual soul or spirit continually until moksa (liberation of samsara and the fourth goal of life). This means that each time a soul is born, it can improve itself, the cycle of transmigration continues (reincarnation) until one overcomes avidya and desires nothing.

Once the soul reaches this stage, they no longer struggle with the cycle of death and rebirth. Since we now know that life does not end at the death of the physical body, but the soul lives on, with each reincarnation, the soul comes one step closer to perfection: Mokṣa (मोक्ष), also called vimoksha, vimukthi, and mukti.

After a series of successful reincarnations, the soul becomes mature enough to no longer require a physical body. The soul instead continues to evolve in inner planes of consciousness until it gets released. This release from samsara or karmic impressions is known as moksa. Moksa is said to have occurred when our soul has successfully evolved, extraneous karmic imprints have dissolved, and God is fully realized.

Chapter Six: The Eight Fold Path of Yoga

Patanjali's yoga sutra is often called aṣṭāṅga (अष्टाङ्ग) where aṣṭā means eight and aṅga, limb. Aṣṭāṅga yoga is both a specific yoga tradition and one that covers all aspects of yoga philosophy. The author of aṣṭāṅga yoga is Maharishi Patanjali, the same author of the Patanjali yoga sutras.

The aṣṭāṅga scriptures were said to have been written at about 200 BC, although there are arguments that original copies of the literature are a few thousand years old. These scriptures started as an oral tradition passed down by memorization or rote learning of the verses from one generation to another. In the 15th century, the teachings were presently known as Raja or royal yoga. The yoga sutras are categorized into four sections called pāda (पाद), namely: Samadhi pada, Sadhana pada, Vibhuti pada, and Kaivalya pada. Aṣṭāṅga yoga falls into the sadhana pada category.

The eight limbs or eightfold path, like medicine for the soul, serve as a prescription for ethical and moral conduct and self-discipline. The eight limbs are not a step by step belief or discipline for improving spiritual nature but are a multidisciplinary perspective which must be practiced in tandem with each other or developed together for self-realization. Practicing meditation helps the yogi or devotee develop in these aspects. The eight limbs of yoga are:

1. Yama (restraints or don'ts)
2. Niyama (spiritual observances or do's)
3. Dharana (concentration)
4. Samadhi (superconscious state)
5. Pranayama (breath control)
6. Dhyana (meditation)
7. Asana (posture)
8. Pratyahara (withdrawal of the senses)

Patanjali classifies yama, niyama, pranayama and asana into **bahiranga yoga** while dhyana, samadhi and dharana fall into **antaranga yoga**. Pratyahara is the link between the two.

Yāma (यम)

The first limb is a Sanskrit word that means "bridle," "curb," or "restraint." In this context, it implies self-control and discipline. It is also an interpretation of behaviors that influence our attitudes towards others. These yāmas destroy desire and negativity to transform humanity into something divine. Practicing yāma fills the heart with light, cosmic love, and harmony. There are five yamas. They have a distinct order and form the bedrock of samadhi. The five yamas are listed below.

1. **Ahiṃsā(अहिंसा):** This is the first yama because one must first rid themselves of their barbaric nature. Only then can one develop cosmic love and be able to practice yoga. Ahiṃsā simply means non-violence. It does not permit cruelty to man or animal in any manner or for any reason.

This yama implies more than just kindness; it is thoughtfulness and consideration for other people, animals, and things. It is positive love in totality. When practicing ahiṃsā, you must not wish harm, whether through unkind thoughts or looks to beggars, animals, and servants as it is hiṃsā — cruelty. Under hiṃsā also is watching another suffering pain unjustly or approving cruelty towards others.

> **2. Satya(सत्य):** This means truthfulness. In life, it is not always desirable to speak the truth on all occasions as it can cause harm to another unintentionally. Satya urges one to express the highest truth but do not be disrespectful about it. The whole self is the truth. The twelve forms of truth practiced by the unselfish include equal vision, charity, disinterested philanthropy, compassionate harmlessness, truthful speech, self-control, forgiveness, and an absence of envious emulation, self-possession, endurance, modesty, and lack of jealousy.

Your truth should not be unpleasant, harmful, or portray any falsehood. If the truth will have adverse effects on another, it is better to stay silent, so our words do not conflict with ahiṃsā. There is a belief that when someone speaks the truth only for twelve years, they acquire Vak siddhi, and whatever such a person says will come to pass. Once you are established in truth and honesty, all other virtues embrace you.

> **3. Asteya(अस्तेय):** "Steya" in Sanskrit means "to steal." Asteya is the exact opposite. It is a yama that teaches us not to be covetous or take anything that is not ours. It also means that when placed where another entrusts something to you or brings you into their confidence, you do not betray or take undue advantage. Asteya is a form of self-restraint because whatever is not yours by right is fueled by desire (Kama) or thirst (Trishna), which attracts bad karma in this lifetime and the next.

4. Brahmacharya (ब्रह्मचर्य): This is the most controversial yama, the one that gets the loudest gasp in a room full of students. Brahmacharya means "flowing with brahma." it is a practice that implies celibacy and overcoming the desire for sex.

Brahmacharya is a practice that helps you grow and maintain your energy if you keep it to yourself. This is because when you have sex or get intimate with someone, you give aspects of your energy away and are not at your full potential. Abstaining is a practice prevalent in power sports such as football, wrestling, and boxing, where aggression is a desirable trait. Aggression may not be considered desirable in yoga because of ahimsa, but there is another catch to staying celibate.

Many experts on spiritualism and kung fu opine that sex drains one of inner energy or chi, robbing you of motivation and competitive spirit. Arguments may fly for or against the viewpoint. Still, the fact remains that one round of sex can demand about 101 calories (men) and 69 calories (women), meaning that an average of 3.6 calories of energy is burnt every minute of copulation.

We all love pleasure as humans, so a vow of celibacy is a tough pill to swallow, even for those committed to yoga. Brahmacharya helps the yogi retain energy reserves filled with Ojas (the energy form for focus and clarity). Stack up enough Ojas, and you project Tejas (personal light) to the universe. Not all yoga masters are strict with celibacy.

Masters like Swami Satchidananda advocate sex if it occurs between two people in a true partnership. To him, partnerships like these help people become happier and more productive. So instead of total abstinence, Satchidananda preaches moderation not just in sexual intimacy but also in work, food, sleep, and drink. Brahmacharya sets reasonable limits for us to become the best version of ourselves. This way, we don't become over-indulgent and lose sight of the things that matter most.

5. Aparigraha (अपरिग्रह): A, in this case, means "non," a negative connotation. Pari means "from all sides," and graha means "to grab or take." Aparigraha, the last yama, means not taking more than what is needed. It is the opposite of Parigraha, which means "to seize."

Aparigraha involves more than just managing covetousness. It is showing respect for man and nature. The 21st century has taught man to exploit everything to the point of overindulgence so it shows gross disrespect for the gifts nature has provided us. This yama is the clarity of mind that differentiates want from need.

There is nothing unlawful or sinful about harboring a desire if it does not supersede a need. Often, the lines between wants and needs are blurred, so we abuse people, take beyond our means, cheat, or force a situation in favor of a desire.

Aparigraha requires the support of the other yamas. It stops the fear of loss, untruthfulness, hatred, theft, anger, depression, lust, etc., and restores peace and contentment.

There is a Sanskrit phrase that goes, "Nothing is mine" or "Not for myself but for you." This principle might sound simple, but it encompasses the entire universe and is a form of Īśvarapraṇidhāna or total devotion. The code of idam na mam brings man one step closer to aparigraha because one who serves selflessly will obtain samadhi.

Even the Bhagavad Gita talks about aparigraha when it teaches that devotees should leave behind all their possessions that pose a hindrance to the path of yoga. I am not advocating that you shave your head, wear sackcloth, and give your house away. What I advise instead is to find balance and use what you do have judiciously.

Niyama (नियम)

Niyama is the second limb of Patanjali's yoga sutra. Niyama means laws or rules for personal observance. It differs from its counterpart yama in that while yama teaches about attitudes toward others, niyama is more personal and involves our attitudes towards ourselves. The niyamas are listed in the sadhana pada verse 32 and are five in number thus:

1. **Śauca or Shaucha (शौच):** This means cleanliness, purity of speech, mind, and body. Śauca is the same as suddhi (शुद्धि). The yoga sutras make it clear how vital it is to keep the body and mind clean and pure so we can grow in mental clarity (sattva), continue to have good feelings, and always be cheerful in attitude (saumanasya).

These allow us to focus intently (ekāgrya), mastery and union of the senses (indriya), ensuring a readiness or preparedness (yogyatvāni) for self-realization (ātmadarśana).

Śauca is both internal and external purity. External purity helps generate inner purity by ridding oneself of negative emotions, granting the devotee serenity, poise, and happiness when done vigilantly. Practicing śauca allows one to forego physical attachments, making it easier to practice brahmacharya gradually. One way of instilling inner purity is by practicing asanas and pranayama.

2. **Santosha (संतोष):** This translates to happiness, contentment, or modesty. We live in an age where the mind is continuously drawn to perceived needs. The endless pursuit of what we feel we want makes us extremely disappointed when we don't get what we desire. For this reason alone, many fall into depression and contemplate self-harm or suicide in extreme cases.

Disappointment, depression, and suicide are a few examples of events that happen because we lack the discipline of contentment. We fail to see that even lack has a purpose and could be karma. Santosha teaches us to accept our fate instead of craving for one thing or another and complaining about what we don't have.

The yoga sutra teaches that "From contentment, the highest happiness is attained." Enlightenment only descends into a contented mind as it is the mystic stream of happiness that calms the three fires of samsara. Santosha is the only antidote for the cankerworm that is greed and is one of the four sentinels guarding the door to moksa. The others are Satsanga (wise company), Vichara (inquiry), and Shanti (peace).

3. **Tapas (तपस्):** This means asceticism, austerity, or purification. Before I go into details about this yama, I would like to tell you the story of a jeweler I admire so much- Lluis Masriera. Ever seen how gold pieces are made? Lluis heats the rough dirty looking nuggets to a temperature of 1000-12,000 C. this temperature separates the metals in the alloy so the gold sinks to the bottom to be collected. Other metals and impurities are then left behind.

When cold, the gold is heated even further and placed in a mixture of nitric and hydrochloric acid for further purification. After this, a lab's analytical methods help determine how many karats (purity) of gold before formation into gold bars. Lluis claims each unique piece takes at least six weeks to make and, at most, a few years.

This example illustrates how we move through life, collecting impurities (klesa). We are purified by the furnace that is tapas. We are reminded of our original nature, Atman, ever pure. According to Alistair Shearer's commentary on Patanjali's sutras, tapas is about inner alchemy; it is a transmutation process in which we burn all imperfection and leave behind only purity.

Tapas is the act of keeping the body healthy to confront and handle inner cravings without outward show. This way, we heat the body and, like gold or other metals, purify it.

Tapas comes in many forms, from paying attention to what we eat and how we carry ourselves, to breathing patterns, etc. It helps one develop discipline, so we don't eat, for instance, when we are not hungry as gluttony is punishment to the body.

Tapas prevents us from subjecting our body to diseases like shortness of breath, obesity, high blood pressure, etc. Like we have established, tapas means restraint or purification. Austerities, such as observing silence and fasting, help increase discipline. Detoxifying the body isn't easy, as it is uncomfortable to shed toxins and other superficial layers to help evolve beyond the yogi mat.

4. Svadhyaya (स्वाध्याय): This is a study of the Vedas, introspection, and self-reflection. Sva is a Sanskrit word meaning "self," and adhyaya means examination. Svadhyaya means "get close to something' or "study yourself." This niyama teaches us to center ourselves and stay non-reactive to the dualities to purge our souls of unwanted and destructive tendencies.

Svadhyaya is continually asking the question, "Who am I?" This form of introspection is indirect satsang because you can be in situations where the direct company of the wise is impossible. Self-study clears doubts and elevates the mind, filling the soul with sattwa as we progress in our journey to self-realization.

5. Īśvarapraṇidhāna (ईश्वर प्रणिधान): The root words of Īśvarapraṇidhāna are īśvara (ईश्वर), and praṇidhāna (प्रणिधान). This last niyama is the very core of yoga. A surefire way to be devoured by our ego, to remain spiritually stagnant is to choose a life with no devotion to the divine or the almighty, and to spurn his will for our lives. Your ego will want to fool you into thinking you need no one but yourself to make whatever you desire to happen, but Īśvarapraṇidhānserves as a reminder you can do nothing on your own and you need as much help as you can get -- and there's nothing wrong with that.

Think of Īśvarapraṇidhāna as a call to devote yourself to a greater power and to dedicate yourself to a cause much grander than your existence. You might be tempted to assume that such a total surrender means being weak, but that is not the case. You are indeed one with The All, and you are one with the divine will of the cosmos. The only thing it is for you to do after giving your best is to leave it up to God, communing with him in prayer, trusting that you will receive the best of solutions.

Think of the niyamas like compasses for your spirit, as they guide you along your way, showing you how to keep yourself pure in body and mind. With this viewpoint, as you continue with your practice, it gets easier. You grow in strength which cannot be contained or constrained by your human nature.

During the following chapters, we will dive into the rest of the yoga paths.

Chapter Seven: Asanas, Pranayama, and Pratyahara

Āsana (आसन) is a Sanskrit word meaning posture, position, or seat. According to Patanjali in the yoga sutras, "The meditation pose should be steady and comfortable." The verbal translation of the word asana is "abiding or staying." In yoga, the body is a temple or vehicle for the spirit, its care vital for spiritual growth. Thus, asana has proven to be the way a person experiences the unity of mind and body.

Many asanas are derived from animals' movements and natural positions and bear the names of such animals. For example, Marjari (cat pose) that elongates the spine and stretches the body, Shashankasana (hare pose) to aid relaxation, and Bhujangasana (cobra pose) to help let go of emotional turmoil and aggression are examples of raja or royal asanas.

Each posture is dynamic in the sense that the yogi is perfectly centered between activity and non-activity, tranquility, and movement. Each asana is a creation of a mental masterpiece, a physical prayer that, once we master, helps us handle the dualities of life.

As you stretch in yoga, consider the sutras 11.47, which clarifies that the way to perform asanas is through loosening up (Śaithilya), putting in the required effort (Prayatna), and meditating solely on the limitless (Ananta).

Śaithilya helps the mind discard its many barriers so there is a perfect state of unhindered balance. This way, the asanas serve the dual purpose of exploring the conscious and unconscious mind. Breathing plays a significant role in asana. Coordinating body movements with breathing patterns makes for a harmonious yoga practice that stimulates the body's temperature, metabolism, and circulation.

With asanas, the breath improves muscle relaxation by consciously expanding and contracting tense areas of the body to create a calm, clear mind. Asana is both a step in preparing for meditation and a form of meditation. Sri Patanjali teaches that asana and breath control will create equilibrium in any organism's energy flow, creating a fertile field for the spirit to evolve.

Asana and Gymnastics: Similar or Different?

At first glance, it may seem like gymnastics is similar to the poses in yoga. Iyengar observed asanas as practices that "create steadiness, health, and lightness of limb. "Asanas create endurance and healthy and agile limbs to allow mental equilibrium and forego fickleness of mind.

True, asana and gymnastics require flexibility and strength, but there are key differences:

> • Gymnastics and yoga demand balance, endurance, and flexibility. However, gymnastics requires a truckload of agility that does not cut across all age groups, unlike yoga, which can be attempted by both little children and the aged.

- Gymnastics is more of a physical sport, but yoga develops both physical and mental faculties.

- Yoga teaches one to discard the ego, accept our limitations, and be in the moment. Gymnastics, on the other hand, is extremely competitive.

Benefits of Asanas

1. Better flexibility and improved muscle strength.

2. Increase circulation and strengthens the spine for better posture

3. Overall better mental clarity and emotional health.

4. Healthier eating and lifestyle that promotes self-care.

5. Eases acute and chronic pain since most poses are in synchronicity with the breath.

6. Stimulation of the nervous system, organs, and glandular activity.

Prāṇāyāma (प्राणायाम)

The foundation of Prāṇāyāma comprises the Sanskrit prāna, which means life force, and āyāma, which means to regulate, extend, control, draw out, or restrain. Yoga Sutra II.49 states, "Tasmin sati śvāsapraśvāsayorgativicchedḥ prāṇāyāmḥ" or that [firm position] being acquired, such movements of inhalation and exhalation must be controlled. This is prāṇāyāma.

Prāṇāyāma, movement toward prana, involves measured and controlled breathing to control the energy within a living being to restore balance and promote health. Controlling breathing is synonymous with maintaining vital life force because when inspired breath meets expired breath, the air is directed inward to the body's energy system or chakras, primarily upward to the crown chakra.

Pranayama is vital to the practice of yoga. It is closely associated with asana. In the Yoga Sutras, pranayama and asana are described as the most effective purification methods and a means of self-discipline for the mind and body. Asanas and pranayama produce sensations of heat — Tapas, the inner fire of purification. Then the tapas also works to purify your nadis, eliminating all the impurities within (Nadi shuddhi). The nadis are basically your body's subtle nerve channels. When cleansed, there is a direct result on the body and the mind.

The Three Main Modifications in Prāṇāyāma

Prāṇāyāma, as described by Bhattacharya and Iyengar, consists of three breathing exercises performed during Saṃdhyā. Regulating the breath comprises:

- Inspiring air or Pūrak
- Retaining air or Kumbhaka, and,
- Expiration or Rechak

Kumbhaka is further classified into Bahya kumbhaka (retention following inhalation), and Antara kumbhaka (retention following exhalation).

Breathing modifications or phases are also given by Patanjali, who describes three main types of pranayama:

- Bāhya vṛtti or inhalation
- Ābhyantara vṛtti or exhalation
- Staṁbha vṛtti or breath retention

Yogi enthusiasts and beginners learning prāṇāyāma are taught bāhya vṛtti at first as it is safe and comfortable. Only after they have mastered this technique can they be taught the method and benefits of ābhyantara vṛtti. These three practices are performed in succession after achieving the desired asana, but variations of these above-listed techniques exist according to kāla (time), saṁkhya (count), and deśa (place).

Kāla refers to how long you retain the breath. Saṁkhya is the number of counts that go by after you inhale and after you exhale, while deśa indicates the center of your attention while breathing, whether it's your third eye, the middle or higher regions, or the spinal base.

The Fourth Prāṇāyāma

This prāṇāyāma is said to be beyond the other three and is called kevala kuṁbhaka or ākṣepī. This pranayama, or kumbhaka, is far outside the realm of that which is within, and that which is without. When you break down this sutra, it looks like this:

- Bāhya = External
- Abhyantara = Internal
- Viṣayā = Sphere
- Bāhya-ābhyantra = Breath retention following exhalation
- Abhyantara-viṣayā = Breath retention following inhalation
- Akṣepī = Surpassing
- Caturthaḥ = The fourth

During pranayama, yogis move from one experience to another, from the less refined to the more subtle levels. At first, kumbhaka (breath retention) requires effort after antara kumbhaka or bahya kumbhaka. Soon after, the total suspension of breath becomes spontaneous and even natural (Sahaj).

This stage is called kevala kuṁbhaka, and it can happen at any point between inhalation and exhalation. Many people think this phenomenon impossible, but it happens in day to day life when we experience a glimpse of kevala kumbhaka when our minds are in a state of single-pointed focus. Think of times you've experienced breathtaking sights or immense bliss, surprise, or shock, or when you hear a beautiful musical piece or find yourself in spectacular scenery.

Air is the chief medium of prana. With each breath, we absorb cosmic energy- Life's power and the prime element of consciousness. Prana is also found in food, which is why devotees understand the importance of a healthy vegetarian diet. Eating animals is considered as hiṃsā.

Myths claim that the length of a person's life is preset by the number of breaths, which is why the practice of pranayama teaches the yogi to preserve time and lengthen life span by taking deep calm breaths.

Your body has an aura. This aura is formed by prana. Your body also has nadis, which are channels that allow the flow of subtle energy or prana, and are thousands in number. Your body also has chakras, which are centers of concentrated energy. How much prana flows, and how well it flows through these chakras and nadis will affect your state of mind. Prana represents the vital energy source needed by our physical and subtle mental layers.

Consciously guarding the body's airflow increases vitality, immunity, inner peace, mental focus, and detoxification. The quality and quantity of prana and its flow via the nadis and chakras influence one's state of mind. When prana levels are high with a steady rhythm, the mind is at peace, even joyful.

If you fail to pay attention to the breath, you will experience blocked nadis, and your prana flow will be broken. Often, this break is caused by worry, tension, conflict, doubt, and fear. Even science has proven that you first fall ill in your subtle body before you experience the illness in your physical one.

Since kevala kumbhaka does not involve inhalation or exhalation, it is considered the last stage of samadhi or spiritual union. Kevala kumbhaka enthusiasts propose this form of pranayama has numerous health benefits, from cell regeneration to the longevity of life. As the yogi trains their breathing and prana forces, kumbhaka becomes more refined and effortless. In time, they progress to Chaturtha, which does not involve breathing at the physical level.

This evolution happens along with the changes in our perception and the subtle change in pranic forces. You can only experience chaturthah when you have mastered prana, just like the great yogis and yoginis who effortlessly carry out kumbhaka and keep their senses (Dharana) suspended. The practice of breath control leads to the next limb of yoga, pratyahara, which is the withdrawal of the senses.

Benefits of Pranayama

On the benefits of pranayama, Patanjali teaches Taṭḥ kṣīyate prakāśāvaraṇam. As a result, the veil over the inner light is destroyed. Inner light, is prakasa, which is infinitely hidden but never destroyed. Without prakāśa, we identify with the mind or body and feel mortal.

Prāṇāyāma enables us all to understand pure consciousness and the One, thereby removing the veil of thoughts and mental darkness- āvaraṇam. This is the only way we can reduce the density of the mind to practice dhāraṇā as written in the sutra "dhāraṇāsu ca yogyatā manasḥ."

Prāṇāyāma increases your energy levels by enhancing the quantity and quality of prana. It heightens your spirit and expands your aura by clearing subtle energy channels and centers of your body. It influences your state of mind and guarantees a positive and calm outlook when done correctly. You make better decisions and cope with mental blocks better. Prāṇāyāma harmonizes all the channels of your physical body and promotes mental, emotional, and physical toughness.

Some Examples of Pranayama

- Nadi Shodhan pranayama or anulom-vilom pranayama (alternate nostril breathing technique)

- Bhramari pranayama (bee breath)

- Bhastrika pranayama (bellows breath)

- Kapal Bhati pranayama (skull shining breathing technique)

- Ujjayi Pranayama (ocean breath)

- Simhasana Pranayama (lion breath)

- Suryabhedan pranayama (right nostril breathing)

- Sheetali pranayama (cooling breath)

- Sheetkari pranayama (hissing breath)

Pratyāhāra प्रत्याहार (Retraction or Withdrawal of the Senses)

This is formed from two Sanskrit words, Prati- प्रति, meaning "against, away, retreat or withdrawal" and āhāra आहार, meaning "nourishment or food." This limb of yoga involves drawing in one's awareness. It is the process of sensory withdrawal from external stimuli or that which brings nourishment to the senses. It does not imply closing your eyes to the world, but the mental fortitude to retract from it taking back control, so you are not pulled back and forth like a puppet on a string.

Swami Sivananda believes that pratyahara is yoga itself and is the most crucial limb in sadhana. Pratyāhāra is synonymous with the first stage of ṣaḍaṅgayoga taught by Buddhist Kālacakra tantra, which also teaches the withdrawal of the senses and their replacement with mental senses from an enlightened deity.

According to Patanjali's teaching, pratyāhāra is the link between the external aspects of yoga (bahiranga) consisting of the yamas, niyamas, asanas, and pranayama as well we parts of yoga antaranga or internal yoga. After pratyahara has been internalized, the yogi can consciously sever the link between the mind and the senses. This ensures that the sensations from sense organs do not alert their respective centers in the brain.

This action will lead to a seamless entry into Dhyana(meditation), Dharana (meditation), and samadhi (mystical absorption), marking the movement of the devotee's inner state from the outside to the inner sphere of the spirit, the end product of which is the aim of yoga. Pratyahara is closely associated with dharana. When performing pratyahara, the devotee withdraws the senses and mental faculties from external distractions.

In dharana, our attention is focused on a singular object such as a figurine of a deity or mantra. Thus, it can be said that pratyahara is the positive side, dharana, the negative of the same spiritual focus. Pratyahara is vital to yoga as it is the practice that allows one to gather their thoughts to wade through the narrow channel that leads to enlightenment.

When absorbed in the act of pranayama, pratyahara happens automatically. But even with sensory detachment, the mind is not asleep. It can respond. It chooses not to do so. We can know the circumstances and events, but we can concentrate without being swayed. Like the tortoise that withdraws into its shell, we can be in the world yet not of it.

In today's world, our senses have become our masters rather than our servants, and as a result, most of the emotional imbalance we undergo is of our own making. This chatter prevents us from achieving inner peace since we burn so much mental and physical energy trying to suppress unpleasant sensations. For this reason, pratyahara is regarded as sensory transcendence. It offers us an opportunity for introspection and sensory cultivation to determine what habits are detrimental to our spiritual progress objectively.

In yoga, there are three levels of ahara or nourishment. First is physical food, which brings in the material elements necessary to nourish the body (water, earth, fire, ether, and air). The second ahara comprises the subtle substances or impressions that feed the mind, such as sight, touch, taste, smell, and sound. The third ahara nourishes the soul. These come in the form of our associations, which affect us with the gunas of sattva — rajas (hyperactivity or distraction), sattva (peace and harmony), and tamas (lethargy or inertia). Freeing our mind from ahara grants our minds a spiritual immunity level that helps resist negative sensory influences.

Forms of Pratyahara

There are four significant forms of pratyahara. They are control of the senses - Indriya pratyahara; control of works - karma pratyahara; control of prana (prana pratyahara), and mind retraction from the senses (mano pratyahara).

1. **Indriya Pratyahara:** This is a basic form of pratyahara since the mind can be as willful as a teenager. The influence of the media has made controlling our senses sound foreign and impossible. Every day different media outlets bombard our senses with bright colors, fashion choices, food, and every kind of sensory indulgence you can imagine. Our minds continuously buzz from day to day sensory bombardment, dominating our flesh with endless demands making us prisoners of the external world to forget our higher purpose. Indriya pratyahara gives us the weapons we need to bend our spirit to our will, not suppressing it but motivating and adequately controlling it.

2. **Prana Pratyahara:** Also called control of breath or prana, this is used to control the senses. When prana is scattered, so are the senses. Controlling the senses helps in

shaping and tuning the subconscious mind. Ayurvedic teachings state that constantly exposing the senses to mental impressions daily is akin to overloading your mind with toxins. After a while, your bad mental hygiene, like fat and toxins, will clog your mind and lead to mental lethargy and illness.

3. Karma Pratyahara: This is the control of actions done via controlling the motor organs. Motor organs react to different external stimuli through the sensory organs. The act of motor control helps in the withdrawal of the mind. Once you learn to surrender selflessly to the divine, doing work to benefit others instead of self, you are practicing karma pratyahara.

4. Mano Pratyahara: This is the withdrawal of the mind. This form of pratyahara involves controlling one's attention span. Once the mind is retracted from numerous sensory inputs, it is put under control so external disturbances pose no influence.

Chapter Eight: Vibhooti Pada — Dharana, Dhyana, Samadhi, and Samnyama

Dhāraṇā (धारणा): Fixation of Attention

Dhāraṇā, according to the sutras, is "the mind's fixation on a particular point in space." Dhāraṇā aims to steady the mind through focus on a single stable entity. The word dhāraṇā comes from the Sanskrit root word dhr- धृ, which means "to maintain or hold." Here, dhāraṇā means introspective and single-pointed focus. This is a form of meditation similar to receptive concentration.

Consider a case of artificial irrigation. When farmers dig trenches to water their fields, the grooves serve as channels away from the main reservoir. These trenches are usually the same size and are dug in different directions, each a branch of the main body of water. If one track is broader or deeper than the others, more water flows through it. This analogy is the case in dharana. We fashion the conditions for focus.

Once we tune our minds to focus in one direction, the focus becomes more intense, and as such, other flutters of the mind melt away like wax in the heat. There are different practices to ensure a single-pointed focus:

- Directing your eyes upward and holding them in place as though focusing on a spot in your forehead's center.

- Directing your eyes downward as if concentrating on your solar plexus or navel.

- Directing your eyes forward to focus on an area that corresponds to the bridge of your nose.

Static objects such as a mantra, the silent repetition of a sound like OM, or the image of a deity may also be useful. These practices are effective because they serve to stop the mind from wandering from thought to thought or memory to memory since the mind is singularly focused on a static object of choice.

If you focus on a single energy center or chakra, you can sense mental and physical barriers in the system. This ability to focus depends on prime health and integration and should not be considered a cure of sorts or an escape from reality; instead, one should see dhāraṇā as a practice that helps realize consciousness.

With each stage preparing us for the next, practicing pratyahara is the doorway that leads to concentration-dharana. Pratyahara relieves us of external distractions creating a fertile ground for dealing with mental distractions. As we continue dhāraṇā while applying the practices of asana and pranayama and pratyahara, we learn to manage our continually drifting focus and become self-observant. Extended periods of dhāraṇā give rise to meditation. This task is easier said than done.

Dhyāna (Pali: झान, Sanskrit: ध्यान)

This means reflection, abstract meditation, or contemplation. The root of the word dhyāna comes from the Sanskrit root word dhyai, which means "to think of" or dhi, which in Vedic scripture, means "imaginative vision." The term dhi is used in describing the goddess Saraswathi endowed with the gifts of wisdom, knowledge, and poetic eloquence. Dhi later evolved into dhya and dhyana, which mean contemplation.

Thomas Berry describes dhyana as sustained attention and applying the mind to a specific point of concentration. Swami Vivekananda describes dhyana as a state where the mind is trained to remain affixed on an external or internal location such that the power of focus flows in an unbroken current towards that point.

For instance, if you focus on a subject or idea, dhyana is a nonjudgmental observation and reflection of the subject in the form of an uninterrupted train of thought. It is a seamless flow of awareness that considers the subject in all forms, consequences, and aspects. The choice to practice dharana could fall into one of two groups: Sakala and nishkala. As a sadhaka (seeker) in sakala, your focus is on the attributes or saguna and the attribute-less nature (nirguna) of Īśvara. As a sadhaka in nishkala, you focus your attention on reality and it's all-pervasive nature.

Dhyana implies that the yogi is not conscious of the act of meditation. It is an awareness of the consciousness of being. In this situation, dhyana rouses puruṣa or atman, the fundamental level of being and the ultimate reality to attain bliss or liberation. This is why dhyana is the limb that separates māyā from reality culminating in samadhi or union with a source.

Like all other limbs in yoga, meditation or contemplation is tricky to master as it is a systematic process requiring patience and practice. This is because meditation aims to quieten the chatter of the mind, including normal mental activities like sensory stimulation, imagination, and memory.

Of the three, memory is the toughest to quieten. It is a puppy that refuses to sit still no matter how many treats it is given. However, using mantras and single focus makes it possible to silence memory to break through to a state of total awareness.

When you practice dhyana, love flows in and through you. This divine love possesses a vibrational frequency that transcends the confines of the human mind. The ego falls away like scales in dhyana only after you fully surrendered to the divine will. Achieving dhyana is not by willpower. The more you seek it, the easier it slips from your grasp.

Achieving this seventh anga (limbs) of yoga will require dedication to the other six anga. This way, like a rose in bloom, dhyana will seek and eventually find you. When physical posture, breath control, and suspension or control of the senses are practiced along with dharana and samadhi (absorption) or the internal limbs of yoga practice (antaranga), it is called Samayama (संयम). Samayama is the concept of integrated and concentrated meditation that leads to an increased sense of self-absorption and the termination of all mental modifications.

Samayama is a Sanskrit term that means "tying up, integration or binding." It is the simultaneous and continual practice of raja yoga's innermost aspects, namely, dharana, dhyana, and samadhi. While the other limbs of yoga sanctify the body, samayama sanctifies and prepares the mind. Samayama implies a state of total mind control. The complete removal of the mind from worldly attachments leads to greater insight concerning the object of meditation. Dhyana, in this case, supersedes single focus of the mind (eka-tanata).

The Difference Between Dhyana and Awareness

When one is "aware," at least one of the senses' functions are in tandem with the mind. In dhyana, all senses and sensory inputs are silenced while the mind alone remains active. The reason is that in dhyana, the mind is centered toward atman.

Awareness has a point of termination associated with creating or seeking knowledge with some spiritual wisdom, such as listening to scripture to develop physical and mental experiences. But dhyana is a journey beyond experience, one that exists at the ultimate pinnacle of reality. We lose ourselves in this journey to break old samskaras while practicing complete vairagya.

In awareness, we travel beyond the mind's realm. In dhyāna, we are aware of our mind and its workings. This is because we have become one with self or Atma, as pure consciousness is the driving force behind all principles guiding the machinations of the mind and body.

The Link Between Dhyana and Samadhi

Dhyana can come with listening to scripture (shabda), prayer, repetition of a divine name (nama-japa), or praises to God (kirtana) to create a favorable environment for the spiritual journey. Dhyana is perfect when the conscious and unconscious powers of feeling (bhavana shakti), action (kriya shakti), and thinking (chintana shakti) merge into a single state of consciousness. This fusion allows the union of the knower (jnata), the object of knowledge (jneya), and knowledge itself (jnana). This union is known as samadhi.

In Shashthopadesha written by Gheranda Samhita, Sri Gheranda teaches his pupil Chandakapali the three types of dhyana, namely:

> 1. **Gross meditation or Sthula Dhyana:** This is the total contemplation on a divine entity; more specifically, a sacred image or a personal deity (ishtadeva) or the image of one's master (guru).

> 2. **Subtle meditation (Sukshma Dhyana):** This is the polar opposite of Sthula Dhyana. In this form of meditation, you contemplate on an abstract form or object such as a geometrical shape (yantra), the coiled serpentine force at the base of the spinal column (kundalini), a sacred syllable (mantra), a vital being (prana), or inner music (nada). These

are conducted in shambhavi mudra, where the eyes are half-open yet focused intently on the mind within.

3. **Luminous meditation (Jyotirmaya Dhyana):** In this form of meditation, you are to put all of your attention on your Atman, which is your supreme, pure self; or you focus on your soul (jivatma), paying attention to the light that radiates from your heart chakra. Constant practice allows the seeker to see the light reverberating in her (pranavatmaka Jyoti). Meditation in this form of dhyana is done using a bright object such as the moon, stars, light from a candle, or any other item recommended by your guru.

According to sage Gherand, jyotirmaya dhyāna is a thousand times better than Sthula dhyāna while sukshma dhyāna is more advantageous compared to jyotirmaya dhyāna. According to Chhandogya Upanishad in chapter VII. 6.1-2, meditation is as natural as the earth and sky itself; however, the range of meditation goes only as far as the object's range meditated upon.

If you meditate on absolute reality or brahman, your mind can move only as far as the range of brahman. If speech is your object of meditation, the mind will only travel as far as speech permits. However, when the choice of meditation is the omniscient self, using faith, truth, and reflection, meditation will open the doorway to the knowledge of self-existent universal reality, which is neither above nor below but within.

Samādhi समाधि -Fully Integrated Consciousness

Samadhi is the final step of ashtanga yoga. Patanjali describes it as a state of pure, undiluted ecstasy. In yoga sutra III, Patanjali teaches "tadevārthamātranirbhāsam svarūpaśūnyamiva samādhih." When translated, it means that when the individual becomes one with the object so nothing save for comprehension is evident, it will seem as though the individual has lost their identity. This complete absorption with the object of understanding is known as samadhi.

In the book, The Wisdom of Yoga, Stephen Cope describes samadhi as the total union between subject and object where no seam is left showing." Samadhi is the union of two Sanskrit words sama- सम meaning "together" and dha- धा meaning "to place." Samadhi is hence defined as a stage of intense concentration that results in integration or absorption with ultimate reality or consciousness. By this stage, we have become so absorbed in the object of meditation that our mind becomes fused with it. Only then can we say we have attained the state of samadhi.

It is important to understand that the freedom in samadhi results from transcendence from the shackles of ego. Your true self is free from the trappings of Kleśa and the bondage of karma, all of which are a byproduct of samskaras and vasanas (desire). All these negative feelings conflict with samadhi as they entertain the idea that you are separate from atman. Seeing clearly and equally from the mind with no bias or conditioning from habits or preferences, without a need to judge or suffer attachment is bliss.

Samadhi helps you realize your essence as a divine creator and plunges you into the purest state of being. As you go about your day to day life, you are no longer worried about the past, present, or future. All you are and all you do is mindful awareness of each second regarding every passing moment as a sacred act.

In that state of samadhi where nothing exists anymore, this unity shows how we become an entity with the object of our choosing and realize what it feels like to be an entity devoid of difference, how our soul can enjoy bliss and pure awareness of this identity. The conscious mind seeks and finds the unconscious oblivion, which terminates at a point where the soul is finally free. This stage is known as kaivalya pada, a term used interchangeably with emancipation or mokṣa. Once the soul attains this state, it never returns to bondage.

There are various stages of samadhi, depending on whether the seeker has transcended the object of meditation and is resting with or without support from any form of consciousness. Attaining samadhi is not something one can do on a whim. One cannot choose to practice dharana.

Certain steps must be simultaneously taken for one to master each limb of yoga, and the same goes for samadhi. The mind must be still, free from external chatter to enter into dharana. Failure to do this has grave consequences. For this reason, yoga sutras suggest practicing asanas and breathing techniques to prepare for dharana, then delve into dhyana before samadhi can occur.

As we reach pure bliss or ananda, we discover our worries fall off like old skin. We gain clarity of mind and supernatural gifts (siddhis) such as complete control of the senses, bilocation, power over life and death, clairvoyance, and so on.

Pseudo-Samadhi

Samadhi eludes those actively seeking it. This is counterproductive because enlightenment is what we all seek. This search for eternal bliss forces people to turn to pornography, drugs, gambling, shopping, gluttony, and other destructive habits. While these habits offer temporary pleasure, they create karmic debts that plunge us to lower depths even though the fleeting high feels so good.

Practicing the eight anga of yoga liberates us from not only bad habits but the confines of social and cultural conditioning. The discipline offered by yoga takes us one step closer to kaivalya so that even if we don't obtain samadhi in this lifetime, we die as better evolved beings.

True Samadhi is not a permanent state of being. According to Patanjali, the mind must be pure and ready with no mental impressions. Only with purity of mind does one get to experience samadhi for a longer period and attain mukti, mokṣa, or kaivalya.

The perfection that is samadhi glorifies every aspect of the true self by exposing them to the light of knowledge. Attaining samadhi does not rid you of your individuality; however, it frees you from emotional attachment to it. Samadhi is difficult to explain in words. It is a unique state every individual must experience for themselves.

Chapter Nine: Application of the Yoga Sutras in Today's World

The yoga sutras of Patanjali is one of the core foundational texts of yoga belief. The first teaching in the sutra begins with the verse "atha yoga-anuśāsanam," which means that now yoga is shared. This verse reminds us to commit to yoga's daily practice and inculcate the teachings into our lives and relationships with others.

One may wonder why instructions as old as two millennia are essential in the 21st century. The answer to this is simple. The sutras contain ancient wisdom, and as far as we know, knowledge has no expiry date. The sutras contain insight on how we can live better, practice patience and self-awareness in our fast-paced world. Below are a few reasons Patanjali's teachings are evergreen:

1. **Yoga Helps Us Understand the Meaning of True Happiness (Ahimsa):** The benefits of the sutras are two-fold. We not only grasp what happiness means, but the teachings also cast a light on the factors that knowingly or unknowingly form barriers to happiness. There is no end to the strife in the world of today. Every second of the day, there is news

about war, hunger, and strife. All this information and these occurrences only disturb our peace.

Friends and strangers alike rage at each other. Peace talks in different countries are broadcast on television, yet people can't help feeling scared walking down the street. The root of these problems lies not outside but within ourselves. This reason is why the sutras stress the need for non-violence (ahimsa), the most crucial of the yamas. World peace will forever remain a utopian concept until the world is filled with individuals who collectively strive for peace.

The sutra teaching non-violence states, "In the presence of one firmly established in non-violence, all hostilities cease, and enmity is abandoned." Ahimsa is not merely a rule for us to follow. It is more than suppressing cruel tendencies. Ahimsa is the realization of the amazing potential inherent within us, the potential to treat all with reverence, so we give no room for violence to arise. Ahimsa does not mean remaining passive to violence. It is remembering the interdependence and interconnectedness within the cosmos. For this reason, you make a daily effort to show love, forgiveness, and respect for others, initiating the change we desperately need to see in the world.

Tips to Cultivating Ahimsa and Finding Happiness

- Take out time to make someone's day. This person can be a friend, relative or total stranger. Pay for someone's coffee or bus fare, buy a burger for a homeless person.

- Lend a helping hand or a listening ear to someone sad or in need.

- Make peace with someone you have mistreated.

- Watch your inner monologue and dialogue. Mindfulness is a house built one thought at a time.

- Practice positive self-affirmation. Replace harmful, demeaning opinions with thoughtful, loving ones.

- Let an aggressive driver have the right of way.

- Learn to let go and forgive yourself.

2. Yoga teaches vital lessons that remind us to stay faithful to ourselves and our purpose in life (Satya): Satya means truthfulness. You can have goals and to-do lists a mile long, but if you do not approach life from the perspective of truth, even the simplest tasks will feel like a burden you are ill-prepared to bear. Today's world is chock full of untruths, beliefs, and opinions from people that do not have a clue of what it feels like to walk a mile in your shoes.

The 21st century sells lies faster than the simplest of truths, and because we all struggle for acceptance, we live our lives seeking validation from others while hiding behind the cloak of lies we have become used to. Yoga sutra 2.36 teaches us the importance of living, speaking, and being our truth. According to Swami Satchidananda, when one is established in the practice of truthfulness, actions and reactions bend to his will. Whatever such a person says will come to pass in due time.

Go back to the last conversation you had with someone. What did you think about? Were your actions or reactions based on your truth or on something you were desperately trying to avoid? The truth isn't something that can be forced or fabricated. Learning yoga transforms us, so we approach our relationships not just from the point of meaning and intimacy but from the point of vulnerability and truth.

Satya is discovering your truth on and off the yoga mat. Satya manifests in different ways; in our bodies, we can identify real sadness as a feeling of tightness in our chest, anger, a twisting or coiling of the abdomen, and resentment like a large boulder on the shoulders. Satya helps us better understand and communicate our needs and emotions because we have accepted the truth about how we feel.

Embracing Satya through yoga requires us not to be defensive or feel threatened when another person lives authentically or says something that is true but is displeasing to us. Satya is keeping an open mind, understanding that honesty is worth the risk, taking responsibility for our actions, and believing in our intuition when the rest of the world cannot prove its veracity.

Satya is letting go of our biases, surrendering our agendas, and the quest for power using manipulation so the divine can guide us within us. As a devotee, you learn that not all truth needs speaking. This is because right beside integrity is the gift of tact. You will discover that telling the truth is just as crucial as being sensitive to other's feelings. When in doubt on how to proceed, there is always the option of Mauna (silence).

Tips to Cultivating Satya and Living Our Truth

● Tell the truth more often. Catch yourself each time you are about to tell a white lie or half the truth. The only exception to this rule is when the truth will affect another adversely. Here, stay silent. Silence, in this case, is rooted in the spirit of goodwill.

● Observe your speech for a day. Are they necessary? Kind? Edifying? Only speak when your words meet these criteria.

● Practice taking the vow of silence for a few minutes or an hour, depending on your schedule. This will ensure that when you do speak, you do so from your most authentic place.

● Listen closely to your body. Not for signs of ill health but for signs that portray the truth of feeling or authenticity of emotions. Are you smiling while you feel a tightness in your chest? Keep track of your changing emotions to build confidence in your inner guidance system.

3. Yoga teaches us to manifest prosperity without stealing from others (Astheya): How aligned are you with the spiritual laws of prosperity and manifestation? Do you know that the door to abundance is built on the sutra of astheya? Sutra 2.37 states, "Asteya pratisthayam sarva ratna upasthanam." Translated, this verse means that wealth comes to the yogi established in non-stealing.

Stealing does not always mean holding a weapon to take from others or breaking and entering. Astheya is seen in a plethora of life situations. We are thieves when we slack off at work. Taking extra time after lunch to do things unrelated to work or an emergency is using company funds or resources for purposes far from what you are paid to do.

Showing up late to appointments and sending verbose emails steals other's time. Talking about people behind their back counts as stealing their good name. Guarding your emotions in a relationship steals time from people who want to love you. Stealing another's idea equals stealing their gifts and an opportunity for them to make something of themselves.

The purpose of astheya is to look mindfully at the countless ways we take that which does not belong rightfully to us. Yoga helps us understand the fulfillment that comes from selfless service. We forget our egos with yoga and put aside our desires to serve another expecting nothing in return.

When we practice Seva (selfless service) that springs from the practice of idam-na-mam, we discover pure and boundless joy. We can motivate ourselves to do good because we know that giving love takes nothing from us; we now operate from the mentality of abundance.

Tips to Practicing Astheya and Selfless Service in Our Daily Lives

- Think of something you have and value. Think of someone who you feel needs it more than you do. Offer them that thing and evaluate how this feels better than giving away something you don't value or need.

- Be generous with your time and attention. Instead of always being in a hurry to do something, offer a listening ear, a smile, a word of advice, or shoulder to cry on.

- Practice generosity with your patience. Don't think patience is a virtue that runs out, because just like our true selves, the qualities we possess are boundless and infinite.

- Take up any position within your community to do volunteer work. This could be anything from animal shelters, working in a nursing home, or a soup kitchen. The goal is to give back to the earth that has already given you so much.

4. Yoga impresses on us the need for restraint, self-control, and moderation (Brahmacharya): Sri Patanjali stresses the need for moderation in sutra 2.38 "Brahma-carya pratiṣṭhāyāṁ vīrya-lābhaḥ-," meaning, "When one becomes steadfast in abstaining from in sexual continence, they gain spiritual energy." This sutra does not just teach about celibacy but self-control and moderation in all things. Yoga helps us understand the advantages of living a balanced life emotionally, mentally, and physically.

Everyone these days wants more; more wealth, more connections, enhanced body parts, etc. Yoga helps us see the truth: Humans only desire more because of avidya even when they know that more isn't always better. When we expend energy in one aspect of our lives, say material or physical achievement, we get burnt out and lack resources to cater to other parts of our life such as spiritual growth and mental health. Even athletes understand the need to pace themselves before a major competition.

Practicing yoga and studying its principles stop you from depleting your life force and energy in ways that do not matter. It teaches us all to manage the resources we do have in ways that foster peace of mind.

We can practice brahmacharya by practicing moderation in eating, as gluttony forces our bodies to use a lot of energy in digesting food only to suffer inertia, lethargy, weight gain, and disease.

When we overthink, we get depressed and might become driven to take our lives. Decide what you want to give your life force to and dedicate a set time for it, no more, no less. This mindful thinking is the thermostat that warns us when our energy levels are running low so we can find our balance point.

Tips for Cultivating Brahmacharya and Practicing Moderation

- Monitor your savings and expenditure. Make wiser financial choices. Cut out the stuff you don't need, and have a garage sale to auction out all the junk you have saved in your attic and basement. Stop squirreling away things you don't need.

• Guard your energy wisely. Don't speak unless it is called for. Don't hang around toxic people or energy vampires. Set boundaries for yourself, time, space, and energy. No one should make you do more than you are willing to. You alone teach people how best to treat you. Blur your boundaries, and you spend the rest of your life having to defend instead of acting on your priorities.

• Find your rhythm. Don't build your life or schedule around scientific research, your pet, or your alarm clock. If you are bright-eyed and bushy-tailed only when the sun comes down, OWN IT! I am not saying you should ditch work and convert your week to an extended weekend. All I advise is that you find your preferred time for work, rest, and make changes to honor your favored rhythm.

• Do you have a list of goals or activities you are yet to complete? Discover which projects are necessary and commit to those only. Self-control is the key to accomplishing your goals.

• Find out what or who drains your energy the most. Re-evaluate, delegate if necessary, and discard what needs discarding. Please pay attention to the signals your body gives when energy levels are at their lowest.

• Watch and control your temper. Refer to the principles of ahimsa and satya.

5. Yoga teaches us the power of gratitude (Aparigraha): Have you ever been thirsty? Not the "I-think-I-need-a-diet coke" kind of thirst. What I mean is the kind where your eyes feel dry, red and hollow, your lips are chapped and peeling, and your voice is so hoarse you could drink a cup of your urine. If you have ever experienced this or can imagine it, then imagine being offered being offered a sippy cup of cold spring water.

You are grateful for the promise of a drink before it even comes. And when the drink comes, you cherish every sip. Every gulp tastes so good. This consciousness of gratitude is known as aparigraha. Aparigraha is lacking in the world today, which is why we treat everything with contempt. We don't fix; we replace.

The concept of aparigraha is taught in yoga. It magnifies our happiness by helping us appreciate the blessings surrounding us. It teaches us to spot opportunities for growth at every turn, no matter the circumstance.

If you had two dollars and gave them out to two random kids and only one showed gratitude, which one would you give more money to next time? Appreciation brings more of the good things you desire.

Sutra 2.39 teaches that once we rise above our fear and envy, we cultivate the habit of appreciation and understand life's real purpose. Aparigraha is a catalyst for abundance, but there is a catch: Aparigraha is a cultivated trait. It is not dependent on any circumstance you are in at any given moment. Gratitude comes from our deep-seated belief in abundance, which creates our experience of it. When you live life in such a way you continuously count your blessings instead of repeatedly thinking about lack, we reaffirm our ability to manifest abundance even in the most unlikely of situations.

Tips for Cultivating Gratitude in Our Daily Lives

● Give more to receive more. You always receive twice as much of what you put out to the universe.

● Practice the art of positive flooding. Tell someone you know everything you feel is pleasant about them. You can also practice positive flooding on yourself. Many people have found this helpful in dealing with low self-esteem issues.

• At the end of each day, or right before bedtime, write down or think about at least five things you are grateful for.

• Before purchasing something new, ask yourself if you are buying just because you don't have it or it is something you desperately need. Do your purchases have a genuine purpose or are they purchased because of greed or envy?

6. Yoga teaches us to embrace the beauty in simplicity (Sauca): What does it mean to choose simplicity? It means clearing our minds and space of clutter, purifying ourselves mentally, emotionally, and physically. Simplicity is honoring only thoughts and deeds that matter. When we do this, our hearts and souls find joy and a more profound sense of awareness.

It's challenging to live simply in a world like ours, powered by stress plus fast-paced living. Simplicity taught in yoga helps us reject the culture of consumerism and insatiable desire. How many social media accounts can we have? How many health supplements are too much?

The philosophy of sauca is not living in some ashram or taking a trip on a time machine to times when life was simpler. Sauca is the decision to live in the complexity of the present without losing sight of one's true self, the divine self within us. Materialism has crept into our consciousness leading us to become unintentionally attached to things like what we do instead of who we are. As a result, we end up seeking happiness in all the wrong places.

We fear staying silent, being bored, being boring, or considered simple. We forget that creativity can be heightened in boredom and that the most fantastic ideas in the world come from people who have mastered the art of doing nothing sometimes.

Because we have complicated lives, we have forgotten the simpler pleasures, those that bring true bliss. Before rushing to get your coffee cup, have you taken some time to watch the sunrise at dawn? I assure you it is so breathtakingly beautiful that your heart might stop for a millisecond.

Tips for Cultivating Simplicity in Our Daily Lives

• Instead of wishing for extra hours in a day, declutter your to-do list, so you don't have to multitask so much.

• Make a list of simple pleasures. Engage in activities that cost next to nothing. You can wake up a bit earlier and take a walk instead of the bus to work (if you work nearby). Appreciate the weather and the lovely sights you see along the way.

• Create a space that embodies sauca in your home or place of work. Fill it with love, light, and positive energy. Let no one or anything invade it. Let this space remind you of how sauca makes room in your life for joy to find you.

• Abide by the SIMPLE principle Stop, Inquire, Mindfulness, stay Present, Listen and Love, Enjoy. Living this way ensures your actions bring only the purest joy.

7. Yoga teaches us that sometimes contentment is the greatest happiness (Santosha). This lesson taught in sutra 2.42: "Saṁtoṣāt-anuttamas-sukhalābhaḥ." This translates to "Contentment brings about unsurpassed happiness." Ever heard the serenity prayer? It is a prayer asking God for the serenity to accept the unchangeable, the courage to effect the changes we can, and the wisdom to tell them apart. Like

221

the prayer rightly points out, there are things in life set in stone and others within our influence.

The sutra about santosha in verse 2.42, encourages us to accept things as they are and seek wisdom to discern what can be changed and what should be left alone. For many people, practicing contentment feels like a cop-out. That's not the case. Choosing contentment, no matter the circumstances, does not mean passivity. It means we are willing to grow in life positively without the influence of attachments. Always whining about things that bother us is resistance, and that causes suffering.

There is no bulletproof vest in life against negativity, random tragedy, or mean ill-treatment. We can only choose how we wish to react instead. Our reactions will determine if we are setting up positive or negative karma for future lifetimes. Be content with your body size, practice contentment when you fail at something, choose not to complain, or lose confidence in the face of failure because forgiving your weaknesses is the greatest show of strength.

Tips for Practicing Contentment in Our Daily Lives

• Sit under a tree or anywhere in nature and savor the contentment that comes from the sound of the breeze rustling through the leaves.

• When something happens that isn't to your liking, take a deep breath and exhale. In your exhale, let go of your worries and accept all things as they come.

• When asked to perform a task, especially one you do not care for, practice doing it with a cheerful attitude, going above and beyond what is required. Catch your judgmental thoughts. Switch to a more accepting demeanor and note how acceptance makes you feel.

8. Yoga teaches us to persevere in challenging times (Tapas): In sutra 2.43, Patanjali urges us to combine a disciplined life with a life of passion. He also teaches the necessity of austerities such as breath holding, the vow of silence, and fasting. These spiritual practices may seem a bit much, but passion is like fire. For it to be wielded for the purpose of creativity instead of destruction, then some measure of control is necessary.

The sutras teach the difference between willfulness and will. The former is a will that is out of control. Constant training of words, thoughts, and actions are skills required by a true yogi. This discipline of will is the training that is tapas.

Tips to Practice Self Discipline and Perseverance in Our Daily Lives

• Cultivate an active practice of right and considerate action. Seek the mental blocks you have and surrender your will to clear a path for yourself going forward.

• Choose soft-spoken speech even when you are burning red hot with anger. Note the difference you feel from regulating your voice instead of getting carried away by your emotions.

• Keep an eye out for negative habits and when they come up, shock your mind by reacting the exact opposite way. This will get rid of the terrible nature of bad habits.

• Make time to identify your purpose in life (dharma) and consider how your unique nature might benefit others.

9. Yoga opens our minds to our true nature (Svādhyāyā): Introspection is humbling every single time. It never gets old. Introspection is what you pay your expensive therapist for. You get to sit down on a comfy couch and answer questions that make you think deeply for an hour.

The sutra on Svādhyāyā urges us to look within and discover our innate personalities and our divine self. After this, we will go a step further and identify with our divine self, which is one with others and the universe. Do this instead of identifying with our individual selves. Through introspection, we can be guided by intuition, which provides the best answer for life's troubles.

Tips to Help Us Unite With Our True Selves in Daily Living

• Practice looking outside-in daily. Check-in with your individual and divine self to ensure their purposes align.

• Practice staying in solitude. Get rid of the electronic noise, cell phones, televisions, computers, etc. Seek inner guidance in your choices and actions.

• Write your personal mission statement. This could be on a post-it note, a journal, or as a reminder on your phone. This statement must reflect positive affirmations on who you are, what you want to be in the world, and the changes you wish to effect.

• Do some "light" reading. Read sacred texts like the Bible, the Bhagavad Gita, or yoga sutra translations. Find the one you resonate with and study it deeply.

• Learn to live every day like you know that even your smallest actions have a ripple effect and influence the world. This helps you adopt a more mindful approach to living.

- Look at everyone and everything as a mirror through which you can discover something about yourself. Ask yourself daily, "How does this virtue I appreciate or this vice I detest in another reflect an aspect of me?"

10. Yoga reminds us that surrender is the ultimate freedom (Isvara pranidhana): Tapas, Svadhyaya, and Isvara pranidhana form the transformative aspect of yoga called kriya yoga. We have seen the importance of discipline and contentment in spiritual practice, but even those can become very boring when done without devotion. Devotion provides us with enthusiasm needed to follow the other life lessons taught in yoga.

Devotion makes us choose to intentionally tread the path, to give time, energy, and our lives in the practice of seeking the divine. The sutra of devotion in 2.45 helps us understand that love is not only a feeling but a way of life and spiritual practice; one that forces us to acknowledge shared consciousness in all beings. Practicing yoga deepens our human relationships and well as our relationship with the divine.

Tips for Practicing Devotion to God in Our Daily Lives

- Build a simple place of worship or an altar with items that represent your connection to the divine.

- Make a mental note of where your actions come from. Do they spring from a well of fear, ego, or love? Only act on those feelings rooted in love.

- Offer everything that you have and are in service to divine love. Let your actions be for the greatest good of all involved.

- Learn to surrender to love to help you tap into shraddha (faith, inner strength) so that step by step, you surpass your challenges.

Helpful Tips for Daily Practice

Start Simple: There are a lot of positions that can be adopted by beginners. Do not do too much too soon. Do not attempt complicated postures because you fear the simple ones offer little or no benefits. Remember, it is not only the poses that provide the benefits but the level of focus. Thus, simple poses like the cat-cow pose and the butterfly pose can get you transcendental levels of bliss with single-minded focus.

Longer practice does not always mean better: Would you accept a challenge to run for three miles if you have never jogged a day in your life? It is the same with yoga. Sometimes 1 to 2-hour sessions can be unrealistic and more difficult to maintain compared to a 30-minute burst. Do not copy others in doing longer stretches. It is your journey, after all. Don't feel guilty about the time you put in. Science states that the average person can only remain focused for 18 minutes at a stretch, so why push yourself for an hour when your mind will be elsewhere?

Do not attempt all the poses at a time: Ayurveda has poses that cater to specific body types. It is believed that everything and everyone comprises five essential elements, namely; water, fire, ether, air, and earth. Everyone uniquely combines these elements, and this composition affects everything from our temperaments to the way we look and speak. The proportion of these elements varies with many factors; the weather, diet, genetics, emotions, etc. Each asana targets a specific element. This is the reason some poses are easy for some and dreaded by others. The tip here is to build your practice around the asanas that favor your constitution and build tolerance.

Consistency is Key: Treat your practice like you would your eating or sleeping habits (assuming you have a strict schedule). Once you designate a time for practice, endeavor to stick to it religiously. With time, your body calls you to practice at that time, even when you forget or are not wearing a watch. Many people do their yoga in the morning to help them get ready for other activities in the day, but your practice need not be in the morning.

The Weather Plays a Part in Determining Your Practice Time: Just because your usual time is 6 AM doesn't mean you have to make your way to the studio or a mat in the winter. You can reschedule your time for practice to one that works for you and your body. Stay flexible — pun intended.

Embrace Your Breaks: Take a day off yoga to recharge. Saturday is your best bet as it is a day governed by the planet Saturn. For this reason, you could have low energy levels compared to the rest of the week. If you must, you could do a mild session but don't expend too much energy.

Leave Your Expectations at the Door: The whole point of practicing yoga is it's simple-to practice. You could have a profound, earth-shattering experience one day, and the next is just meh. Why? You come to the mat with a ton of worries, expectations, and attachments. Your experience on the mat depends on a lot of stuff like if you had a great sleep or are still reeling from the margaritas of last night's shindig.

Remember that the not-so-great days of practice are not because of your lack of talent or effort. Those average days are that way because you can't force moments of bliss. Bliss finds you. Just learn to be in the moment while on the mat. Nothing else should matter. Don't overthink anything else because you are giving negativity fertile ground.

The Coffee-Onion Conundrum: Yoga rules go beyond asanas. They cover certain dietary restrictions. Strict yoga rules advocate for a yogi to lay off leftovers, onion, garlic, coffee, spicy and salty food.

These foods could make us restless, cause mental lethargy and physical numbness. So, is it possible that your extra helping of garlic bread is the reason you can't suddenly get into the dancer's pose? That's up for debate.

The ancient monks were perfectionists. They woke up at the same time every day, ate the same helpings of food from the same utensils, and slept at the same time. This way, they avoided loading their system with mental impressions and choices, which is no help in the practice of yoga. I am not asking you "go monk." All I humbly suggest is that you get rid of factors or food that disturb your digestion and practice.

Don't Let Bad Habits Stop You From Starting: Many people use their bad habits as an excuse. "I need to stop smoking so much before attempting yoga," they say. "I will do yoga, but first, let me lose some pounds." Pardon my French, but that's a lot of bull. Yoga is a way of life, and best believe that when you begin, any habits that are ineffective to the practice will fall off like scales. Accept yourself and focus your energy on your practice.

Do's and Don'ts for the Practicing Yogi

Do...

- Practice on a level floor in an airy place and ensure the room has enough natural light.

- Use a mat, towel, or carpet.

- Practice facing north/east at dawn or south/west at dusk

- Rest for a while in a relaxed pose such as the "child's pose" if you find a pose to be difficult.

- Empty your bladder after practice or during your practice. When practicing, toxins from the organs flow down to the bladder because of gravity.

- Practice in this order: Asanas, pranayama, then meditation.

- Lie flat on your back after finishing asana, stay still for 2 to 4 minutes and take deep, relaxing breaths.

Don't...

- Practice on the bare floor.

- Try to suppress involuntary reactions like sneezing, coughing, hiccups, or thirst.

- Practice too often if you're pregnant or it's that time of the month. Ask your guru for specific asanas that can be done during that period.

- Have a shower or drink water 30 minutes after yoga.

- Attempt any other stressful exercises after your practice.

- Practice yoga in an unclean environment or areas with strong unpleasant odors.

- Do yoga immediately after a meal. Wait for 2 to 3 hours for digestion to run its course.

- Practice in a storm or windy weather.

- Practice when there is a grave wound such as a fracture, dislocation, or sprain.

- Practice if you have recently had any kind of operation. operated Resume yoga only after consultation with a certified medical expert.

Chapter Ten: The Path of Transformation — Karma, Vasana, Siddhi, and Ananda

Karma (Sanskrit: कर्म)

Karma means work, action, or deed. It is a spiritual law of cause and effect where a person's actions and intentions affect the future or quality of life of that person. Good actions and choices lead to good karma or rebirths, and vice versa. Karma is often explained with another Sanskrit term, kriya. Kriya is defined as the activity leading to the efforts and actions, while karma is the executed effort or a consequence of the activity (kriya).

The theory of karma includes not only our actions but the intent behind our actions. The symbol of karma is an endless knot seen in many Asian cultural motifs and the center of prayer wheels for sale in temples. The knots represent the never-ending link between cause and effect.

The Principles Forming the Foundation of Karma

The concept or principle of karma is challenging to define because there are diverse views about the phenomenon of karma in Hindu, Jain, and Taoist schools. Many schools of thought consider karma to be linked to rebirth. Some think rebirth is not essential to karma, while others believe the theory of karma and rebirth is flawed fiction. Whether karma is a law, a model, metaphysical stance, paradigm, or approach is yet to be determined. Three common themes cut across the schools of thought that believe in karma and the concept of reincarnation.

1. **Karma is Related to Causality:** In Hindu, Buddhist, and Jain philosophy, it is agreed that actions executed by an individual affect the quality of life they live. Unintentional actions or actions done with disinterest have no negative karmic impact. The effect of karma may not be immediate but can extend to future lifetimes. When the fruit of karma (visible or invisible) is seen in this lifetime, it is called phala. When karmic fruits extend to future lifetimes, it is called samskara.

2. **Karma is Built on Ethics:** This means that karma has a simple premise. That all actions have consequences both in this life and in the next. Good acts will produce good karma, while evil deeds will have negative karma. It is not in the form of reward or punishment but more of action and reaction or action and consequence.

3. **Karma is Linked to Reincarnation:** Reincarnation is also known as the cycle of rebirth or samsara. Hindus believe that all living things go through samsara carrying the seeds of karmic deeds from their previous lifetimes. This cycle of death and rebirth continues indefinitely until the cycle breaks following the attainment of mokṣa.

Karma in Jain Philosophy

Jain belief systems are the oldest Indian belief systems that exist. In Jainism, karma is dirt or a stain that occupies the universe. They do not consider karma as echoes of the past that find their way to our future. The Jains believe karmic dirt is attracted to the mind because of the strength of the karmic field and the vibrations created by the actions of speech, mind, and body.

Here, karma is nimitta, an efficient cause. The soul is the material cause or upadana, for it is the vibrations of the soul and not our actions that allow the inflow of karma. Like fine particles, karma surrounds our consciousness to affect the life we live in at present.

The Jains teach the three truths known as samyak darsana (right faith), samyak charitra (right behavior), and samyak jnana (right knowledge). In Jain philosophy, there are seven tattvas or truths about karma that makeup reality:

- Ajiva: Non-soul

- Jiva: Consciousness or soul

- Samvara: Obstruction of the flow of karmic matter into the soul

- Nirjara: Dissociation of karmic matter from the soul

- Moksha: Complete liberation or annihilation of karmic debris

- Bandha: Mingling of the soul with karmic dirt

- Asrava: Entry of evil karmic matter into consciousness

There are four types of karma, each with two aspects called arabdha (or sprouting karma) and anarabdha (dormant or seed karma).

1. Sanchitta: The accumulation of every action one has ever taken, from the movement of our bodies to the line of our thoughts in all the lifetimes one has ever lived. Sanchitta is all the unresolved past actions waiting for resolution.

2. Parabdha Karma: The portion of sanchita karma shaping and affecting your current life, actions, associations, and tendencies. Swami Sivananda teaches this form of karma is the portion of sanchita responsible for influencing your present body. It is unchangeable and inevitable as we must all pay for our past debts. It bears fruit, placing certain restrictions on us in this in life, some of which can be seen on our birth chart or horoscopes.

1. Parabdha Karma has Three Kinds: Ichha parabdha (personally desired), parechha (due to the desire of others), and anichha (devoid of desire). For a self-realized yogi (jivanmukta), there is no ichha prarabdha, but parechha and anichha prarabdha exist and await resolution.

2. Kriyamana Karma: This is karma in the process of being made. They are created and added to the storehouse of sanchita karma. It is the karma that unfolds because of our free will and creativity.

3. Agami Karma: This is karma that will occur because of your future actions. Agami comes up because as we try to resolve the karma for our past lives in this life, we unintentionally create new karmas that may never resolve in this lifetime. These are stored and are to be taken care of in future lifetimes.

Resolving Karma

• Each form of karma has its method of resolution. For sanchita karma, the grace blessing of the Sat Guru who prescribes tapas and sadhana and the sustained fire of kundalini in a bid for extreme penance remains the only way the invisible and inaccessible seeds of such unsprouted karmas get destroyed in this lifetime.

• Prarabdha karma is resolved through living and experiencing this lifetime. It ends with death.

• Kriyamana, with the fruits of its actions, is resolved via vairagya and daily devotion and worship and strict adherence to dharma.

Karma and Its Relationship With Vasanas

Each seed of karma generates its distinct level of vibration or force known as a vasana. These vasana are magnetic subliminal subconscious impressions. Love attracts love, malice attracts malice, with each karmic seed, the attraction continues with the force of magnetism until all is demagnetized. Western religions have erroneously associated karma with fate. It is a falsehood to think agencies beyond your control preset your life. Swami Vivekananda believes that we can create our future and master our destiny.

Karma is the right to exercise your free will responsibly. It is the chance to choose between the path of light and darkness. This way, we know that every moment, every word, and every deed is a choice. This grants us clearer awareness and higher responsibility for all that we are and all we do.

Vāsanā -वासना: Vāsanā is a term used in Hindu and Vedic philosophy. Mainly seen in yoga and the Advaita Vedanta, vāsanā means "to remain, dwell, or persist in memory." It has Indo-European linguistic roots and translates to mean past impressions formed that affect present consciousness or perceptions. Vāsanā can also mean desire, inclination, or expectation. It is a karmic impression or behavioral tendency known to influence a person's present behavior.

Latent habitual tendencies or conditioning or Vāsana is often used interchangeably with the word bija (seed) to represent latent impressions that result from actions imprinted in a person's consciousness (ālaya-vijñāna). The accumulation of such seeds predisposes an individual to specific behavioral patterns. This is why some people are kind by nature, no matter what, and others inherently cruel.

According to Patañjali, vāsana are potent concentrations or accumulation of samskaras. Often, vāsana is the notion of desire or want. Vāsanās have the power to drive our psyche unless dissolved by Tapas (discipline and austerities) and Nirodha parinama (the transformation of the subconscious that results in the suppression of citta-vritti).

The predispositions, tendencies, and latencies of our present minds result from the stains or fingerprints left behind by our past lives. These subliminal propensities keep us in a state of constant anxiety about the past and the future. It blinds us to the clarity of the here and now, the awareness of existing entirely in the moment. According to Sat- Chit -Ananda, there are four vāsana:

- Suddha or pure vāsana

- Sat or good

- Malina or impure

- Madhya or mixed

You can enjoy the results of these latent impressions in three ways:

- Involuntary action (Anichha)

- Voluntary actions (Swechha)

- From the actions of others (Parechha)

The whole point behind your existence right here and now is to get rid of all your entanglements with vāsana, or the ever so subtle desires that you've arrived at this place with. Every individual has these stains on the citta to varying degrees.

Forms of Vāsanās

● **Deh vāsanā:** This is also known as an obsession with the body. The endless desire to look good, wear fashionable clothes and jewelry, satisfy our body's cravings, be it food, drink, or intimacy.

● **Shastra vāsanā:** This is an obsession with knowledge. To know things for the sake of knowing whether or not that knowledge is desirable or edifying for spiritual or professional development.

● **Lok vāsanā:** The craving for attention from others. It happens when we do things to get attention. We want to be loved, have control and influence over others.

Controlling and Eradicating Vāsanās

Like everything else in life, vāsanās can be good or evil. When used for personal development and the growth of society, they can be excellent aids. Still, when vāsanās become excessive, we become prideful and use these innate desires to destroy ourselves and others. For this reason, we must identify and control the expression of vāsanās, so they don't cause more harm than good.

Like the threads in a cloth, the mind is a cluster of vasanas; so, suppressing the vasanas is easier than eradicating them. When vasana is suppressed, they are only that way until they manifest two-fold once an opportunity arises. The four methods of destroying vasanas include:

● Sama, or the peace of mind gotten from the tranquility bestowed upon by buddhi

● Restraint of the indriyas or sensory organs

● Svadhyaya and meditation on philosophical books to increase knowledge of the truth. This decreases Deh vasana and Lok vasana. After a while, you engage in deep transcendental meditation and give up shastra vasana also.

- Vichāra or atmic inquiry, which is the ability to discern the real from the unreal.

When the threads of Vāsanās are eliminated, the veil covering the mind also disappears into thin air. The soul becomes drunk in the ambrosia that is brahman, and we attain enlightenment.

Siddhi सिद्धि: This is a Sanskrit word that means accomplishment, fulfillments, or attainments. Siddhis are supernatural or paranormal abilities that are products of continuous yogic practice and advancement through sadhana such as meditation and yoga. The Pali term "rddhi" is often used interchangeably with siddhi in Buddhist literature.

The Visuddhimagga, the path to purification, and the most significant treatise on Buddhist practice explained how spiritual masters manifested magical abilities. Some skills mentioned were walking on water, flying, elemental transformation (changing the earth into the air), etc.

Hanuman Chalisa is a marvelous treatise comprised of over 40 hymns in honor of Lord Hanuman. In the Hanuman Chalisa, there is a verse says of Lord Hanuman, "Ashta siddhi nava nidhi ke data." In other words, Lord Hanuman graciously grants true devotees divine treasures and supernatural abilities. The Lords Ganesha and Hanuman are deities who bless all worthy worshippers, giving them ashta siddhi, and the nine treasures documented in Hindu mythology.

Dipa Ma, a Bengali woman and student of Anagarika Munindra, was an Indian meditation teacher of Theravada Buddhism. Known as the mother of light and the patron saint of householders, she demonstrated some of these abilities. As stated earlier, attaining siddhi is only through the regular practice of yoga and meditation. But yoga to attain siddhi must be done through the association of suddha sattva, which is yoga performed with a clean mind devoid of tamas and rajas that contaminate the soul and mind.

In yogi and Hindu literature, there are two main siddhis:

- Normal siddhis: These contain the forces of the world that transform into elements

- Extraordinary siddhis: These abilities open up the mind to the truth that leads to enlightenment.

Siddhis are not mystical powers left for Buddhists only. Anyone can attain any or some of these supernatural powers if they cultivate sadhana — religious and spiritual cultivation for liberation. For this to occur, the devotee must gain perfection in Sila or the principles of human behavior that promote an orderly and peaceful existence in any community. As a yogi or yogini, you must learn to quiet your thoughts (Samadhi) as this is the only way to attain knowledge (Prajñā). You also have to practice the required trances (Jhana). I should state at this point that not a lot of practitioners can meet all five sila, let alone the other necessary conditions for siddhi.

The Eight Classical Siddhis

Also known as Brahma siddhi or the great perfections. These include:

1. **Aṇimā**: This is the ability to shrink the body mass to a size smaller than the smallest atom manipulating one's body to become so tiny you are almost invisible.

2. **Mahimā**: This is the ability to expand one's body to a massive size. Attaining this siddhi allows the bearer to have powers equal to the one that created the universe. Aṇimā and Mahimā are both called madalasa vidya.

3. **Laghimā**: The ability of weightlessness or being as light as air. Some texts translate this siddhi as Vayu gaman siddhi.

Venerable Pindola Bharadavia is someone commonly cited for this siddhi.

4. Prāpti: The ability to obtain whatever one wishes or desires to own or possess.

5. Prākāmya: The ability to achieve or become whatever one desires. Attaining this siddhi guarantees a flow of magical energy that enables one to take on any form desired.

6. Īśitva: This ability is the supremacy over the forces of nature, organisms, individuals, organisms, and the elemental constituents of the universe.

7. Vaśitva: The control over the forces of life and death. This siddhi owner gains undue influence and power over anyone or creature on the earth's surface.

8. Yatrakāmāvasāyitva: The power to make one's wishes come to pass. In some texts, it is written as Kāma-avasayitva, which is the suppression of desire or satisfaction.

Ashta Siddhi

Ashta siddhis are superpowers innate in every man but underdeveloped until one reaches the state of buddha. They are eight in number.

1. Aavesha: The ability to enter the body of another.

2. Chetaso jnaanam: The power to read minds.

3. Drushtihi: The power to see objects outside the normal visual range.

4. Kanti: Extraordinary brightness or luster.

5. Arthaanaam chandatah kriyaa: The power to control sense organs according to one's will.

6. Shrotram: The ability to hear sounds made at distances inaudible to human ears.

7. Smrutih: Remarkable memory. The ability to remember whatever one wishes and what one has seen.

8. Istatah adarshanam: The power to become visible and invisible at will.

In the Bhagavata Purana of the Vaishnava doctrine, the primary siddhis given as a product of yoga and meditation are:

• **Trikālajñatvam:** Knowledge of the past, present, and future.

• **Advandvam:** This is tolerance to extreme temperatures such as cold, heat, and other dualities. This siddhi is also known as Kaadi vidya. This vidya or siddhi allows the devotee to perform long hours of penance under extreme weather or seasons.

• **Para citta ādi abhijñata:** The power to read minds.

• **Agni arka ambu viṣa ādīnām pratiṣṭambhaḥ:** Immunity to the influence of the sun, water, poison, fire, etc.

• **Aparājayah:** Remaining undefeated by enemies.

Krishna gives the ten secondary siddhis, and they are:

1. Anūrmimattvam: Some texts interpret this as Haadi vidya. It is immunity against bodily needs such as thirst, hunger, and other appetites. Several yogis in the Himalayas have this attribute and can remain without food or water for several days at a stretch. They do not even need to answer nature's call.

This quality allows them to go through long periods of penance, yet their bodies remain healthy. An example of this siddhi is a yogi in Arunachala's holy mountain, who had not eaten since 1990. The monk Swami Trailanga can spend hours underwater in the Ganges river to teach men that human life is not dependent on oxygen, except taken under the guidance of pranayama principles.

2. Dūraśravaṇa: Hearing sounds from a far distance.

3. Dūradarśanam: Seeing things from a far distance or seeing items far removed from the field of vision.

4. Manojavah: This involves being able to move your body to wherever you think of. In other words, this is teleportation and deliberate out-of-body experiences.

5. Kāmarūpam: The ability to become whatever form the yogi wants to assume.

6. Parakāya praveśanam: The ability to move into or possess other people's bodies.

7. Svachanda mṛtyuh: This is the ability to die whenever you're ready to leave on your own terms. Not to be confused with deliberately taking your own life through physical means.

8. Devānām saha krīḍā anudarśanam: This involves being a part of divine recreational activities, like sports and games. The yogi also has the option of witnessing these games.

9. Yathā saṅkalpa saṁsiddhiḥ: The ability to accomplish one's desires to perfection.

10. Ajñāpratihatā gatiḥ: Commands and orders remaining unimpeded.

Astha or primary siddhis are explained by Samkhya Karika philosophy. The eight siddhis which free one from avidya to experience samadhi as listed in the Tattva Samasa by Kapila are:

1. Uuha: Attaining knowledge of the 24 tattvas. The tattvas are the entities responsible for the creation of the cosmos. Knowledge of the tattvas is gained via close examination of the prakriti and vritti (determinable and undeterminable consciousness and nonconscious constituents of creation) due to the samskaras of Purva janma (the attributes imbibed by the soul in past lives).

2. Shabda: The knowledge gained by close association with a knowledgeable and enlightened person or a guru.

3. Addhyayan: Knowledge gained from a devoted study of the Vedas, sacred treatises, and ancillary texts.

4. Suhritprapti: Knowledge from excellent and kind-hearted friends or people.

5. Daan: Knowledge gained irrespective of one's needs while attending to the questions and requirements of those in search of knowledge.

6. Aadhyaatmik dukkh-haan: The freedom from disappointment and pain that arises because of a lack of metaphysical, spiritual, and mystic expertise and experience.

7. Aadhibhautik dukkh-haan: The freedom from pain and disappointment caused by passiveness or attachment to materialistic gains and worldly pleasures.

8. Aadhidaivik dukkah-haan: The freedom from disappointment and pain resulting from ill-fate or reliance on the concept of fate.

Ways to Attain Siddhi

Acharya Patanjali mentions these ways to obtain siddhi in sutra 4.2:

1. Janma: This is siddhi obtained through conception. Some children are born to spiritually enlightened parents who receive these powers by the womb that bore them (genetics). It is also believed that certain people obtain siddhi because of their good karma and previous lives' achievements.

2. Aushadhi: Also spelled as oṣadhi, this is siddhi obtained through herbs and medicinal powders. Hallucinogenic drugs and herbs like LSD, mescaline, and peyote can affect consciousness, granting extraordinary powers for a short while.

3. Mantra: These are siddhis obtained through the constant repetition of incantations or mantras, which are sacred hymns with naturally powerful characteristics. Some of these hymns are found in the Rig Veda.

4. Tapah: This is siddhi obtained because of self-discipline, mortification, and penance. The clouds of avidya reside in the mind. They are warded off using self-discipline and austerities that allow one to receive the five elements of nature.

5. Samadhi: Extraordinary and paranormal powers are granted to those who have attained oneness with consciousness and enlightenment.

Ānanda आनन्द: This is a Sanskrit word derived from "a" which means from sides and "nanda" meaning joy. Ananda translates to "divine joy" or "bliss." It is also the name of a movement founded by Swami Krivananda based on the teachings of Paramhamsa Yogananda.

In yoga belief, God is "sat-chit-ananda (सच्चिदानंद)," meaning truth, existence consciousness, and bliss. Sat-chit-ananda is an epithet used to describe the ultimate reality or brahman. Ananda supersedes the temporal happiness gained from material and worldly things.

Ananda is joy that keeps you in thrall and awe forever. Ananda is found through regular and deep transcendental meditation. With Ananda, you will always have a cheerful disposition in the face of any circumstance.

In the Hindu Vedas, ananda is the eternal joy accompanying the end of the cycle of rebirth. This delight occurs when one is set free from all doubts, thoughts, actions, desire, pain, and suffering. Once a devotee has attained Ananda and establishes in brahman, they becomes Jivamukti — an individual set free from the shackles of the cycle of death and rebirth

The Dvaita Vedanta philosophy from the Bhagavad Gita interprets ananda as the joy derived from good deeds and thoughts and depends on the state of mind. According to the Bhagavad Gita, one with an even disposition will attain and enjoy divine bliss in all aspects of life.

Ramanujacharya, the father of Vishishtadvaita Vedanta, teaches that divine bliss only comes about by divine grace, which is attained by the total surrender of one's will and ego to the divine.

Chapter Eleven: The Mystery of Perception

The word "thought" originates from the old English word "boht" or "geboht," both of which mean "conceived in mind" or "consider." Thoughts refer to covert yet allusive reactions that could arise from within or in response to the environment. Thoughts depend on the level of balance between innate response and external stimuli. In everyday conversation, the word "thought" may denote:

- The product of a mental activity
- The ability to reason and imagine
- A consequence of a single idea
- Unformed or perfect intention
- Anticipation or expectation
- Recollection or contemplation
- An idea reminiscent of a period or place
- The state of being conscious of someone or something

Thought is the function of the brain's ability to create mental maps of information received from sensory organs and the external environment, engage in problem-solving, decision-making, analysis, and data manipulation. The analysis of thought process, decision-making accuracy, learning, memory, attention, language, perception, and problem solving are studied in cognitive psychology.

As commonplace as the talk about thought might sound in today's world, it remains a mystery even to the vast world of psychology and neuroscience. It is still unclear to neuroscientists and psychologists how many neurons fire up during deliberation and conscious thought or why neuroscience can answer questions on mental processes and unconscious thought but not free will.

Biologists, cognitive behavior therapists, neuroscientists, philosophers, and linguists have studied thought processes and perception. None of these fields have come to a consensus on the understanding of exactly how the brain works.

Cognition Versus Perception: The Elephants in the Room

Cognition refers to the mental process involved in gaining knowledge and comprehension. Cognitive processing is a higher-level brain function and includes activities such as imagination, perception planning, and language.

Perception is the sensory experience to and for the world. It represents the brain's ability to identify, organize, and interpret sensory information from the environment. Perception takes place when an object attracts the attention of citta through indriya. The senses transfer sensory impressions to the manas, which is the recording faculty of the mind, responsible for conveying their existence to buddhi (the discriminative faculty) and ahamkara (ego). Ahamkara accepts those impressions as its own and mentally notes them to recall some other time.

Perception and cognition are both mental processes, but the former keeps us in touch with and mindful of our immediate surroundings and present circumstances. The latter is the process of forming opinions, making decisions, and harboring beliefs.

Thought Processes Dissected in the Yoga Sutras

Perception occurs when the mind gets colored by stimuli from the physical world. Consequently, this occurrence makes it appear as though the citta possesses its consciousness. Our consciousness is only "borrowed" reflections of purusa on citta. This is similar to a mirror which borrows sunlight and casts its reflection into a room. This false perception that citta's consciousness (identical to avidya) prevents us from realizing our true identity as purusa.

Sutra I.5 states "vṛttayaḥ pañcatayyaḥ kliṣṭākliṣṭāḥ," which means "the mental modifications of the mind (thought processes or Vritti) is five and can be painful (kliṣṭāḥ) or painless (ākliṣṭāḥ).

Sutra I.6 goes further to explain the exact mental processes, given as Prāmaṇa, Viparyaya, Vikalpa, Nidra, and Smrti. Of the five, only three will be discussed in detail regarding how they affect perception, limit the mind, and create confusion.

Pramāna प्रमाण

Pramāna means proof and is an essential concept of Indian philosophy. Prāmaṇa is derived from the Sanskrit words pra (प्र) meaning "forth" or outwards and mā (मा) "measure or determine." Pramā is said to represent proper knowledge, foundation understanding, or basis. Pramāna is a nominal of the word Pramā and is said to be a means of further acquiring actual knowledge.

Prāmaṇa is found in many schools of Hindu philosophy. It is written as Pramāṇavāda and is related to the concept known as Yukti (युक्ति), the application of knowledge in terms of innovation, reasoning method, or novelty in the solution of problems.

Hindu, Vedic, and Buddhist texts on prāmana analyze why humans make mistakes and act in error, the workings of the mind, its numerous flaws, and how one can reverse flaws to attain correct knowledge.

Pramāna forms one part of three central concepts describing ancient Hindi theory on how accurate knowledge is acquired. The other two concepts are known as Pramātr̥ (प्रमातृ, the knower or subject) and Prameya (प्रमेय, the known or object). Each of these concepts has its characteristics influencing knowledge and the process of knowing.

There are six known prāmanas discussed in Hindu texts. Let's get into them now.

Pratyakṣa or perception (प्रत्यक्ष)

Perception can be internal and external. Internal perception rises from our sense organs and how they interact with the objects around us. External perceptions arise from your gut. It's everything you get from your sixth sense or intuition (Pratibha). According to ancient Vedic texts, four conditions must be met before a perception is deemed correct:

- **Avyapadesya,** which means you do not develop perceptions based on hearsay. Your perception cannot be based on another's perception and considered as true.

- **Vyavasayatmaka,** which means for perception to be proven correct, it has to leave no room for doubt or bias. You can't consider your perception correct based on inferences you make, but instead on pure, objective observation.

- **Indriyarthasannikarsa,** which means you must have directly experienced that which you perceive with your own senses, internal and external before you deem it true.

- **Avyabhicara,** which means a perception that is true, will not change. It is what it is. It will not wander off the true path, and it cannot be used to deceive.

Once your information meets all these criteria, you can consider it nirnaya, which means a definite conclusion or judgment.

Anumāna or Inference (अनुमान)

This involves coming to conclusions or deciding something is true based on what you've observed, or based on facts you already know are facts because of reason and logic. An example of this would be looking at the cloudy sky and assuming it's about to rain.

Lots of Hindu philosophies consider anumāna to be a valid way to attain knowledge. There are three important aspects of inference: Hypothesis, also known as prajna; instance or drshtanta, if you prefer; and last but not least, reason, or hetu.

You can split hypothesis into two:

- Sadhya, meaning the idea that needs to be proven true or false,

- Paksha, which is the premise that sadhya is based on.

You can consider inference as a truth based on conditions if the positive evidence or sapaksha is evident, and if the counter-evidence or vipaksha isn't seen. Other philosophies insist on vyapti, which is basically that hetu or reason has to be the foundation of all inference, no matter the circumstances, both with evidence and counterevidence. When the hypothesis has been proven this way, it is called the nigamana or conclusion.

Upamāṇa (उपमान)

This is a comparison or analogy. It is similar to the statement "as above, so below." This use of analogy is a means to obtain conditional knowledge. The subject of comparison is known as upameyam, while the object is called upamāṇam. The attribute under which the analogy is made is called samanya.

If I say to you, "Your face is as radiant as the sun in beauty," your face is upameyam, the sun upamānam, and beauty is samanya. There are times when analogies are considered reliable and times when they are debatable.

Anupalabdhi or Negative Proof (अनुपलब्धि): Anupalabdhi prāmana states that knowledge involving negatives are indeed very practical and useful, as knowing these negatives still counts as knowledge. By "negatives," I do not mean "bad." I mean such statements as "The sky is not made of cheese and cotton," or "Dinosaurs do not exist in this day and age."

When you're able to prove that a phenomenon does not exist, you can arrive at a valid conclusion and can be classed as sadrupa, which means positive validity, or conversely, as asadrupa, meaning negative validity. Anupalabdhi exists in four forms, as non-perceptions of:

- Cause
- Object
- Effect
- Contraindication

Only two Hindu schools of thought endorse the use of anupalabdhi in the validation of knowledge.

Arthāpatti or Assumption, Derivation Based on Circumstance (अर्थापत्ति)

If you get on a train by 6 AM to a destination 20 minutes away from the train station, arthāpatti assumes you will be at the location by 6.20 AM. No earlier, no later.

Some schools accept this as a valid form of knowledge. Those who are against it say that since arthāpatti is not entirely reliant on direct perception or proper inference, the logic is flawed. You might not get to your destination by 6.20 AM for many reasons; there could have been an accident or a change of route proving the wrong logic of arthāpatti.

Śabda (शब्द)

This is a reliance on the testimony of experts, in this case, shruti in the Vedic scripture. Śabda suggests that even though humans need to know various facts, we cannot know everything in this lifetime. Hence we must rely on those wiser than us or written texts for valid information.

A lot of schools regard śabda a way to acquire knowledge from various sources to enrich lives. Still, the question on everyone's lips is, "How does one establish reliability?" Some say establishing reliability is impossible. Others claim that the information is reliable depending on the source, and śabda is not complete prāmaṇa.

Viparyaya विपर्यय

Patañjali yoga sutra I.8 teaches, "Illusion is false knowledge lacking objective basis." Viparyaya is a Sanskrit word meaning misconception, false perception, absence, nonexistent, or reversed. Viparyaya is a term that connotes the wrong knowledge resulting from false perceptions.

Viparyaya is one of the five kleśa because it is an affliction or erroneous cognition that serves as an obstacle to vritti nirodha (silencing the mind). Viparyaya is rooted in avidya. These misapprehensions lead to ignorance, hate, egoism, fear of the unknown, and attachments. Hindu philosophy believes that asking the mind for aid is one step towards correcting these illusions or misrepresentations.

Viparyaya is not a fantasy or the figment of a crazy mind. The mind is sane when clouded by viparyaya. Examples of illusions seen in our daily lives are when you walk into a room and feel everyone is talking about you. A few might be, but others do not pay you any mind. Thus, your perception is false; it is nothing but the "I-sense," the hallmark of viparyaya.

The misconceptions you perceive are mind modifications known for most of the suffering in human life. Vyasa recognizes viparyaya as the cause of the cycle of death and rebirth, the byproduct of spiritual ignorance caused only by avidya and viparyaya. Yoga is a practice of controlling the body and ridding the mind of vritti through samadhi, forcing the mind to recognize valid cognition and perception.

Viparyaya is most potent when done unintentionally. You need spiritual guidance so you can develop your very own "buddhi alert." You also need Prajñā, or the light of wisdom, by which you can see the best ways to grow and expand in vairagya, become ever more aware, increase your prāmaṇa, and be adept at spotting and avoiding illusions, whether raga, dvesa, or other kleśa. This way, you see things, people, and facts as they are.

Vikalpa विकल्प

Vikalpa is also called doubt, fantasy, imaginary perception, or imagination. Vikalpa refers to situations or ideas that do not exist in reality. In ancient texts, vikalpa has two meanings:

- An alternative from the process of deliberation to arrive at a decision. Here vikalpa has a positive connotation.

- The indecisiveness people exhibit when there is a need to confirm a truth or make crucial decisions. Here, vikalpa has a negative connotation.

In the yoga sutras, vikalpa is described as "Verbal delusion from words devoid of substance." Vikalpa is the mind chatter that arises after hearing a word even when there is no corresponding thought outside. An example of vikalpa is the classic rumor. Rumors arise from a person's distorted and clouded analysis of a situation or person passed on as truth.

The story of the three blind men and the elephant illustrates vikalpa. Placed at different aspects of the elephant's body, each blind man described by feel what they assumed was the animal's best description.

Another example is in the description of abstract nouns like time, compassion, love, or hatred. Time, for instance, is not an object. It is a phenomenon understood differently by different people. Some assume they have a lot of time, while others imagine they are running out. Time, in reality, is infinite, unaffected by our cognition or inference.

Vikalpa, when heard, creates a vritti based on the samskaras in our mind. With effort, patience, and spiritual guidance using yoga, vikalpa becomes replaced by vidyā, the unclouded and unburnished truth geared towards brahman.

The concepts of pramana, vikalpa, and viparyaya show that every individual believes in or accepts facts only when they are in alignment with accumulated learning. Each thought is interpreted differently even among twins from the same womb with the same external influences based on illusion (viparyaya), conclusive proof (pramana), or fantasy (vikalpa).

Thus, an individual's knowledge here is described as relative rather than absolute. Your thoughts are based on the manner in which you perceive things, whether or not they're right or wrong. The waves of prāmaṇa, viparyaya, vikalpa encompass all thoughts you have incessantly in your life. When you understand the three, you can manage your thoughts even better as you continue with your yoga practice.

These thought waves are all-encompassing and used to classify how people perceive something or someone throughout their lifetime. Therefore, the truth is usually subjective as knowledge is relative instead of absolute. Understanding these thought patterns and how they color aspects of our life can be done through yoga.

Yoga not only helps us control our thought waves, but it also helps us achieve balance and serenity.

Chapter Twelve: The Highest State of Bliss — Kaivalya

Kaivalya (कैवल्य): This is a Sanskrit word meaning solitude, isolation, or detachment. It is a vrddhi derivation from kevala, a Samkhya yoga philosophy which means alone, isolated, entire, absolute, or perfect. Kaivalya is the ultimate goal of raja yoga and represents the isolation of prakriti from puruṣa and the liberation from the cycle of death and rebirth (mokṣa).

In some Upanishad texts, kaivalya-mukti is regarded as the essence of Upanishads and is the most advanced form of mokṣa that grants liberation from this life (jivan-mukti) and after death (videha-mukti). Ancient Upanishad texts describe the state of kevala, or kaivalya mukti in the Yogatattva Upanishad from verses 16 to 18 as the ultimate liberation and the truest nature of self (paramam padam), devoid of parts and stain, destruction, recognition, birth, death, and experience. It is the intuition of intelligence, real existence, and bliss.

Gauḍapāda, the Hindu philosopher and scholar of the Advaita Vedanta school of philosophy, theorizes kaivalya as the nature of isolation and staying detached from others. In this state, puruṣa is distinct and separate from the other three gunas so there is an absence of dukkha (suffering or sorrow), which is natural with the existence of puruṣa.

There are 34 sutras in the yoga sutras of Patañjali in the fourth pada or chapter. These sutras discuss the effect of samskaras left behind by the endless cycles of birth and the purpose behind the need to rid oneself of such mental impressions. The requirement for kaivalya is listed in sutra 4.6, which states that only the mind born of meditation or purified through samadhi is free from the latent impressions of karma and all other cravings.

Sutra 1.48 portrays the devotee or sadhaka who has attained the bliss of kaivalya to be one who has achieved independence from bondage and has acquired absolute true consciousness. This truth or the power of pure consciousness is known as ṛtambharā prajñā, mentioned in the samadhi pada or first chapter.

The impressions that prevent attainment of bliss are described in kaivalya pada sutra verse 10: "As the desire to live is eternal, so are the impressions that are without beginning." Further, In sutra 4.11, it teaches that beliefs are held together by cause, effect, basis, and support, disappearing with the disappearance of the four.

Mastering Kaivalya: The Path of The Kevalin

A person who attains the state of kaivalya is known as a kevalin and is always alone. In this state, the devotee is in a state of self-absorption where the desires are absent, the mind is asleep, and there is no duality or distinction between the knower and the known.

Kevalin achieves liberation not by rejecting or shunning the dualities, but remaining unaffected by them. Neither discarding nor choosing but deciding to stay free from the mind's modifications, embracing life totally without preference.

This state of being alone is brahman. Kaivalya is the state of oneness with brahman.

Achieving isolation for the kevalin is done through inner transformation and purification of self, both of which are practices inherent in yoga's diligent practice. Yoga engages the sadhaka in the mortifications of self, also known as austerities and self-control. This is the kevalin's path: Becoming detached and wholly absorbed in self. Kevalins do not care for the comforts of this world, relationships, people, or pleasures of any kind, but that does not mean they detest these things.

Kevalins express compassion and concern for the wellbeing of others. The only difference between a kevalin and one without self-realization is that the former isn't led by motive. It is easier to express these higher emotions because he is established and self-realized. As a result, they channel their superior nature.

One might think the kevalin a saint. That is a layman's notion. One who has attained the state of kaivalya is attached to nothing, not even ideas. He sees himself in all things, and people, just as a drop of rain in a pond, becomes one with the pond. The kevalin becomes the same with the universal consciousness, nothing more, nothing less.

Attaining the state of kaivalya begins with renouncing the world. This means that one who walks this path must cultivate a distaste for attachments or any kind, be it from relationships, family, and material things. After this happens, the seeker must practice self-discipline in the form of austerities to strengthen his body and prolong his mind's stillness. Once he approaches the state of kaivalya, he will remain stable and undisturbed by the chatter of the world, attuning his senses to silence and discovering peace not by choosing or possessing but by seeking the company of no one but himself.

After this, all boundaries marking you as part of creation are erased, setting you apart from all traces of asmitā, dvesa and raga, and the delusion that is duality.

Seven Stages of the Discovery of Reality

The sutra 2.27 states that seven forms of ultimate insight come to the yogi who acquires discriminative enlightenment. It is best to think of these stages as degrees to discovering kaivalya.

1. **Understanding the Defection Existing in Objects or Things:** This understanding helps one appreciate that things are not perfect or as they appear. It comes to light that everything deemed worthy, beautiful, or virtuous in this world is conditionally valid and temporary at its core. This awareness discovers the pain behind the "pleasures" of this world, and that suffering cannot be avoided while indulging.

2. **The Discovery That There is a Cause of Suffering:** Pain does not materialize from thin air. The law of cause and effect is better understood at this point. One gains control from recognizing the causal root of the pains of life and the troubles of human experience.

3. **Finding the Way Out of the Pain That Exists:** It is one thing to recognize problems and know its cause, and another to discover a solution. This possibility of a cure from the clutches of pain offers great solace and confidence.

4. **The Recognition of a State Beyond All Suffering:** When the stage beyond pain becomes the subject of awareness, coupled with the feeling there is a way out, the soul becomes free.

5. **The Mind Loses Control Over All Consciousness:** This is like being asleep, but not entirely because the true

self is awake. Citta slowly rises from life's slumber and realizes the possibility of a higher experience.

6. The Material of Present Consciousness or Individuality is Pulled Down and Dismantled: This dissolution of the gunas, which is only a complex fusion of rajas, sattva, and tamas, ensures the mind-body complex ceases to operate.

7. Return of Consciousness to Self so That Self is Finally Aware of Kaivalya: In sutra 2.28, it states that yoga is the only activity that can purify the mind, spontaneously manifesting consciousness toward kaivalya (also called mokṣa). This process is explained with the use of the word āviveka-khyāteḥ.

At the final stage comes viveka khyati or perfection in understanding, which widens the hold the substances of nature have over our consciousness. The unrealized have no control over anything because there is an association of self with the cosmic forces of nature via the affirmation of asmitā and weakness of personality.

The limbs of yoga lead to the revelation of knowledge and attainment of liberation. Yoga frees us from the separatist tendencies causing disharmony between us and nature. This dissonance makes us helpless, but we achieve harmony, absolute power, and control when we reach perfection. Caution must be exercised with yoga. Knowledge is only obtained with purity of thought. Hence samayama must be practiced so it brings salvation to the soul or kaivalya.

I strongly suggest you do not dabble in yoga for selfish purposes, like telekinesis, influence over people, or telepathic communication, as it does nothing for your salvation. After a certain point in meditation (samayama), it is possible to acquire siddhi. Still, one must take care to direct our thoughts when such powers arise to prevent our sentiments or emotions from plunging us into an illusion, cutting us off from salvation.

Conclusion

I have wrapped up this book by discussing the ways you can use yoga to deal with vritti, avidya, and vāsanās, which bring us needless pain and suffering in life. Let's review some ways you can remain unconditionally happy.

There are many methods of dealing with the effects of vritti on our consciousness, but one particular method stands out. It is called Sakshi Bhava, or silent witnessing. There are two ways you can practice this. You can engage in **diligent practice**; when you sit in a meditative stance, with your spine relaxed and your body at rest, observe your thoughts, feelings, and emotions but refuse to identify with them.

Do not suppress them. Doing this only means you identify with them, which is the opposite of what this practice aims to achieve. Observe your emotions like you are split into two halves, one half possessing the vritti and the other, a silent witness who observes with awareness.

The other way you can engage in Sakshi Bhava is through daily **practice in activities**. This is a bit more complex to master. You have to observe your daily practices from brushing your teeth to heading out to work. It can get overwhelming. You should practice silent witnessing for short periods at first. In time, you become proficient in Sakshi Bhava, even in your interactions and relationships with others. In Sakshi bhava, your life becomes a movie while you are the spectator watching from a detached perspective. This practice helps loosen the clutches of asmitā, lessens the dukkha of misidentification, and increases contentment.

For overcoming avidya, you can practice **Viveka khyati** or **unwavering knowledge without room for doubt (विवेकख्याति)**. This is a practice most yogi use to keep avidya at bay and suppress the emergence of pratyāya (ideas or contents of the mind) in their state of divine consciousness.

Along with Viveka khyati, practice **para-vairagya** (detachment from materialism). This is the height of mental renunciation. Just like viveka khyati starts from the simplest forms of viveka, developing from prolonged and dedicated practice, para vairagya starts from simple acts of surrender until it reaches its peak in the renunciation of illumination and enlightenment of the atomic plane.

When you do both judiciously, it culminates in the highest form of samadhi: Dharma megha samadhi. This samadhi obliterates the bija of samskaras and unlocks the gates of reality for the eternal dwelling of puruṣa. Dharma megha samadhi then destroys avidya and ends the samyoga of puruṣa and prakriti in sutra 2.23. At this stage, avidya ceases to obstruct the vision of puruṣa that has reached self-realization or kaivalya.

Vāsanās are ingrained habits or tendencies. Getting rid of vāsanā is done using a step by step technique rooted in **pratipaksha bhavana**, which is the application of opposite thought. To deal with vāsanās, put into words a short yet simple statement that identifies the thought behind the vāsanā. It is time to ask the essential questions like, "Does this matter? Why do I want this?" etc.

It helps to note the guna is responsible for the vāsanā. Most times, it is the terrible two-rajas and tamas. Where raja is full of extroversion, anxiety, agitation, desire, and greed, tamas is more introverted, depressed, and ashamed.

Identify the value behind the thought you feel. Do you value a desire to be loved? Appreciated? Do you value wealth and status? When you answer this, ask yourself if this value you placed in high esteem feels authentic to your identity or a value impressed on your psyche by cultural and social conditioning.

Weigh the truth and legitimacy of the thought. All thoughts are clouded by subjectivity and personal interpretation. Are you willing to think outside the box to prove that your thoughts are true?

Measure the cost of keeping this vāsanā alive. How does harboring this habit of yours affect you, your relationships, spirituality, and psychological well-being? If you weigh the price and its impact, your mind will gradually detach from such patterns.

Assume the perspective of atman, the boundless consciousness you have, and are. And ask yourself how you would feel or how things would change if you let go of this pattern or vāsanā.

Apply the opposite thought. Turn the negativity you feel into something positive. If you feel or think of lack, think of abundance instead. If you feel lonely in a relationship or empty from a lack of companionship, believe in your mind you are whole and perfect without it. Replace avidya with vidya to let go of your limitations.

Finally, discover evidence to support your new line of thought. The mind loves habits. That is how vāsanās develop in the first place. For this step to work, you need to find at least three reasons to support your new pattern or outlook.

This requires persistence and diligence because, like a graft, your mind will kick against it at first. But once you have proof of how the new thoughts supersede the old, your mind is forced to accept things as they now are.

With time, your new outlook will become habitual and automatic, allowing you to view mental impressions with increased objectivity and live a life of bliss in its truest and purest form.

One more time: Are you happy?

Here's another book by Kimberly Moon that you might like

References

Ali, S., Balaji, P., & Varne, S. (2012). Physiological effects of yogic practices and transcendental meditation in health and disease. *North American Journal of Medical Sciences, 4*(10), 442.

Ashtanga Yoga - Patanjali's Yoga Sutras. (n.d.). Art of Living (India).

Ashtanga Yoga by Maharishi Patanjali. (n.d.). Temple of Inner Wisdom.

Burke, G. (2012, December 16). *Dharana, Dhyana, Samadhi, and Meditation.* Original Christianity and Original Yoga.

Girl, A. Y. (2019, October 29). *Is A Daily Ashtanga Yoga Practice Enough For Your Body?* Ashtanga Yoga Girl.

Karma, samskaras, vasanas and overcoming fears. (n.d.). Www.Shivarudrabalayogi.Org.

Kaur, M. (2018). *Unit-4 Introduction to Yoga and Yogic Practices.* Www.Egyankosh.Ac.In; IGNOU. http://www.egyankosh.ac.in/handle/123456789/46357

Newlyn, E. (2018, June 14). *The Five Kleshas: Causes of Suffering - Yogamatters Blog.*

Patanjali Yoga Sutra, Ch 1 Sutra 17, Parisamvad. (2013, January 4). The Yoga Institute.

RAJA YOGA Yama, Niyama, Asana, Pranayama, Pratyahara, Dharana, Dhyana. (n.d.). 123himachal.Com.

Samyana - The Union of Dharna, Dhyana and Samadhi - The Study and Practice of Yoga - Chapter 88. (n.d.).

Stewart, M. J. (2017, February 12). *Savikalpa Samadhi (Extract) by Michael J. Stewart.* YouTube. https://m.youtube.com/watch?v=ipHxPwPoafY

The Chopra Center. (2018, May 9). The Chopra Center. https://chopra.com/articles/the-3-levels-of-samadhi

The Concept of Advaita Vedanta. (n.d.). Www.Hinduwebsite.Com.

The Stages of Samadhi According to the Ashtanga Yoga Tradition. (n.d.). Yogainternational.Com.

Tree, S. (2011, November 9). *Patanjali Yoga Sutra 7.* Speaking Tree.

(2013, May 30). *Kaivalya: 12 definitions.*

Made in the USA
Las Vegas, NV
29 March 2021

20309801R00154